# Tomorrow's math

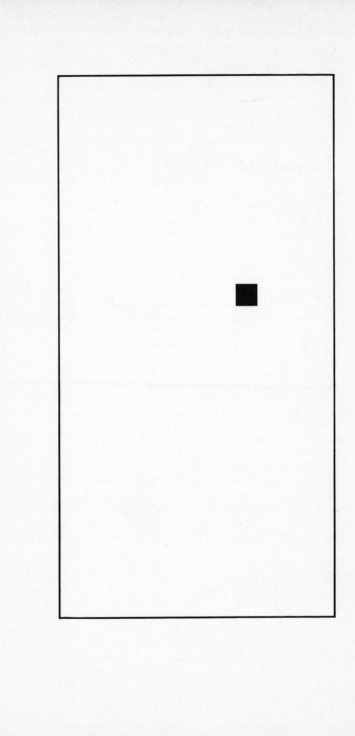

C. Stanley Ogilvy

# Tomorrow's

unsolved problems
for the amateur

New York
Oxford University Press    1962

Copyright © 1962 by C. Stanley Ogilvy
Library of Congress Catalogue Card Number: 62-16577
Printed in the United States of America

# Contents

# Tomorrow's math

# 1

# The meaning
# of an unsolved problem

What is a mathematical problem?

To a mathematician, a problem is often much more than "a question requiring an answer." He may refer to his whole current research project as a problem. If he does, it usually means that he is working on a "good" problem, one which contains many ramifications and subtleties and perhaps ties in with other problems. It may be a mistake to speak of good mathematical problems as if there were also bad ones; but there are certainly interesting problems and dull ones. The most interesting problems are, generally speaking, the ones that are relatively easy to state, have wide application either in mathematics or elsewhere, and possess a certain intrinsic charm of their own.

To say that a working mathematician spends all his time tackling unsolved problems would be a mispresentation unless the idea of a problem is taken in the very broadest sense as *any* mathematical topic. Some mathematicians become so engrossed in one or more specialties that they never bother with separate problems, considering them a waste of time. Others like to look about a bit and are not above trying their hand at any poser which may have stumped a colleague. The fact remains that unsolved problems are a considerable source of inspiration in the field. Although we certainly cannot claim that all or even most of the problems presented in this non-technical book are worthy of such praise, we shall still hope to indicate the kind of lure which some problems hold for the technician, while at the same time offering a sampling of material which can be understood and attacked by the amateur.

□

In elementary arithmetic books one sees lists of exercises sometimes headed *Problems:* "A rectangle measures 5 inches by 7 inches. What is its area?" The "answer" to this "problem" is 35 square inches. A child might obtain the answer by carefully drawing a 5-inch by 7-inch rectangle, ruling it off into square inches, and counting the squares. Thus stated and thus solved, the problem would not satisfy a mathematician, principally because the solution would be of no help in finding the area of another rectangle, say one 6 inches by 10 inches. Thus to the mathematician a solution is usually not an *answer* but a *method*. A better problem is, given the lengths of the sides of a rectangle, how does one find its area?

A still better problem is, does every plane rectangle have associated with it a numerical quantity which can meaningfully be called an area? Note that the previous problem cannot be solved unless the answer to this one is yes. Yet very little emphasis is put upon this last question in elementary mathematics. Its answer seems "obvious": it is taken for granted.

Since about the middle of the last century, mathematicians have become extremely wary of taking anything at all for granted. Accepting something as "obviously true" has led them astray too often. For instance, it is certainly obvious that every piece of paper, like this page, has two sides, in the sense that a bug crawling on one side could not get to the other side without passing around an edge or boring a hole through the paper. Obvious—but false. Perhaps you have heard of a Möbius band. Take a long narrow ribbon of paper, bring the ends together, and join (glue) them to form a ring (Figure 1). If A is brought into coincidence with B, and C with D, then an ordinary

[1]

band results, with an inside surface and an outside surface. But before gluing, give the strip a half-twist, so that A is joined at D and B at C. The resulting surface is a Möbius band: it has only one side and one edge, and a bug could crawl all over it without ever crossing that edge. An interesting (and easy) problem is, does such a surface have an area, and if so, how is it found?

That this matter of area is by no means trivial becomes clearer when we get into curved surfaces. Does a sphere have a surface area? If so, how can it be defined? If it can be defined, how can it be measured? At least partially as a consequence of this question, an extensive non-elementary branch of mathematics called measure theory has been developed. You may think that you know intuitively that a curved surface (the earth's, for example) has an area. But even if the surface in question is smooth, like that of a mathematical sphere, how can you measure it? It cannot be flattened out and hence measured by comparison with a known plane area. The mathematical expression is that a spherical surface is not *developable* from a plane. You may say, "I could paint the surface, measuring carefully the amount of paint used"; but paint has thickness, and by applying a *shell* to the surface you would be destroying the concept of area. To be sure, one has a formula* for the

* $S = 4\pi r^2$. Archimedes considered it his best discovery.

area of a sphere in terms of its radius; but, what confidence can be placed in such a formula until the concept of surface area has been satisfactorily defined?

You probably think that I am only teasing, and that mathematicians have surely succeeded in defining the area of any curved surface by this time. Strangely enough, that is not the case: a simple yet adequate mathematical definition satisfactory for all purposes has yet to be devised. We pursue the matter further in the notes.

Other difficulties arise in connection with volumes of solids. Intuitively it would seem that if you start with a given finite solid object, cut it up into a finite number of pieces, and then reassemble these same pieces in any way, provided there are no spaces anywhere between the reassembled pieces the new solid should have the same volume as the original. In 1924 Banach and Tarski showed that this is not necessarily so by proving the following extraordinary theorem: it is possible to cut a solid sphere into a finite number of pieces and reassemble them by rigid motions (no distortion) to form two solid spheres (no holes), each of the same size as the original one. It might be supposed that the number of pieces in the dissection would have to be very large. But Raphael Robinson has shown that there need be no more than five pieces! These unbelievable results show that we must revise our fundamental notion of volume. There cannot be any completely general definition which will preserve volume under rigid motion—something always previously accepted as "obvious."

□

Perhaps you are beginning to agree that some "intuitively evident" facts turn out to be not facts at all but really difficult problems. Another illustration is Euclid's parallel postulate. Euclid's postulates for plane geometry were originally supposed to be "self-evident truths." Mathematicians today no longer have anything to do with "truths" as universals; they are left to the philosophers. But Euclid's postulates were supposed to be true in the sense that any straight-thinking human being would accept them as obvious ("a straight line is the shortest path between two points," and the like). The fifth postulate, however, dealing with parallels, has a somewhat different flavor. It states, in effect, that through a point not on a straight line one and only one line can be constructed parallel to the given line. People sensed that, if true, this postulate should be *deducible* from the others, that is, could be proved as a theorem. For centuries many mathematicians attempted to solve this challenging problem. The ultimate solution is a negative one: the parallel postulate is indeed a postulate on its own merit, and cannot be deduced from the others. This conclusion was not reached until it was realized, about a hundred years ago, that the problem was being attacked from the wrong direction. If it is only a postulate, one should be able to replace it by some *other* postulate and develop an equally sound geometric system. This can in fact be done. It was unwillingness to face—indeed, inability to conceive—the possibility that there might exist other geometries than Euclid's that clouded the issue for two thousand years. Once this hurdle had been surmounted, progress was rapid.

If an unsolved problem has been on the books for a long time, it is very often difficult because it is being presented in a way in which it can never be answered. The stroke of genius which makes an entirely new approach to an old familiar problem is exceedingly rare. Sometimes, after such a new attack solves a problem, it seems easy and we wonder why no one thought of it before. Usually the trouble was that we had been looking in the wrong direction; often we had been seeking entirely the wrong answer.

One of the three famous problems of antiquity was that of the trisection of an angle with ruler and compass. There are many known methods of trisecting an angle, but the problem was how to do it with only the classical tools, compass and straightedge. For centuries mathematicians sought the wrong answer; for, it cannot be done. Even when this was suspected, the search could not proceed in the right direction until the correct methods were devised. We shall return to this problem presently.

Probably the most successful general method for solving a troublesome problem is that of *embedding* it in a more general context than that in which it first appeared. To cite a simple example, an arithmetic problem may become more comprehensible when treated by the more powerful methods of algebra. The numbers 98 and 102 can be multiplied together by the usual procedure, and the answer somewhat laboriously obtained; but by fitting the exercise to an algebraic form, one can do it mentally. It is only necessary to recognize $(100 - 2)(100 + 2)$ as a special case of $(a - b)(a + b) = a^2 - b^2$ to read off the answer $10000 - 4 = 9996$.

A more impressive example of embedding arose historically in connection with convergence of infinite series. If we divide, by ordinary algebraic long division, we get

$$\frac{1}{1 - x} = 1 + x + x^2 + x^3 + \cdots$$

where the dots mean "and so on." To check that this *might* have meaning in spite of the non-terminating quotient, try multiplying back:

$$
\begin{array}{l}
1 + x + x^2 + x^3 + x^4 + \cdots \\
\underline{1 - x} \\
1 + x + x^2 + x^3 + x^4 + \cdots \\
\phantom{1} - x - x^2 - x^3 - x^4 - \cdots \\
\hline
1 + 0 + 0\ \ + 0\ \ + 0 + \cdots
\end{array}
$$

So it appears to check. However, we must look further at the quotient series. For what values of $x$, that is to say what size $x$'s, does the series converge? It is a geometric progression, and you may recall from your high school days that an infinite geometric progression converges if and only if the common ratio of two successive terms is numerically less than 1. Here the ratio is $x$. If we multiply any term by $x$ we get the next term; hence the series converges, and in fact the limit of the sum is $\dfrac{1}{1-x}$, whenever the numerical value of $x$ is less than 1, written $|x| < 1$. We would not expect a valid equality for $x = 1$ for two reasons: the series $1 + 1 + 1 + 1 + \cdots$ obviously *diverges* (does not approach any fixed number); and the expression on the left becomes $\dfrac{1}{0}$, which has no meaning; we are not allowed to divide by zero. The fraction $\dfrac{1}{1-x}$ does have meaning for $|x| > 1$; but it no longer represents the infinite series $1 + x + x^2 + x^3 + \cdots$ for such values. An adequate warning that things were going bad was given when $\dfrac{1}{1-x}$ "misbehaved" at $x = 1$.

Now, again by long division, suppose we obtain

$$\frac{1}{1+x^2} = 1 - x^2 + x^4 - x^6 + \cdots$$

Once more the right-hand side is a geometric progression, and again it converges only when $|x| < 1$. But this time the left-hand side gives *no indication* that anything might go wrong at $x = 1$. If this value is substituted into the series, it fails to converge; yet the left-hand side becomes simply ½. It was not clear to mathematicians what was going on here until the number system was extended. When the real numbers were embedded in the complex domain then the difficulty disappeared. The denominator $1 + x^2$ equals zero when $x^2 = -1$, or $x = \sqrt{-1}$. In the complex domain, the absolute value of $\sqrt{-1}$ is 1. Thus we have a value of $x$ such that $|x| = 1$ which makes the left-hand side "go bad," just as in the first example, and the warning has been issued not to take $x \geqslant 1$.

We return briefly to the problem of the trisection of an angle. An outline of the proof that such a construction is impossible goes as follows. First one shows that ruler and compass constructions are limited in their scope, in that they can produce magnitudes expressible with radicals *only* if the expression contains a finite number of square roots and combinations thereof but no other kinds of roots. Now if we are given an angle $\theta$ to trisect, we must find $\theta/3$. By trigonometric identities, one obtains $\cos\theta = 4 \cos^3\theta/3 - 3 \cos\theta/3$. Hence if $\cos\theta$ is given, say $k$, the problem is equivalent to solving the equation $4x^3 - 3x - k = 0$, a cubic. This equation is irreducible; therefore its solutions are *not* expressible in terms of a finite number of square roots, and hence cannot be constructed with ruler and compass.

Mathematicians were unable to reach this conclusion by purely geometric considerations. It was by embedding the question in an analytic medium that the result was obtained. To show that a problem cannot be solved is in itself a solution. Thus the classical trisection is impossible, and the problem has been disposed of once and for all.

Some constructions are impossible in a different sense. For example, suppose we are given a straight line with two points $A$ and $B$ marked on it. What is the path of least length which starts at $A$, perpendicular to $AB$, and

[2]

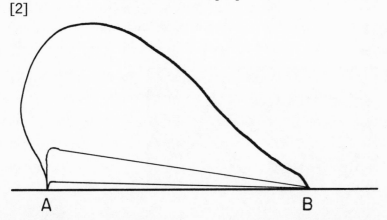

A                                      B

ends at *B*? Clearly there is no shortest path; although the *lower limit* of all possible paths has length *AB*, this lower limit cannot be attained without violating the perpendicularity requirement. Whatever path is chosen there is always another shorter one (see Figure 2). In this example, the non-existence of the sought solution is itself the ultimate solution.

A less trivial example of this kind is worth mentioning. What is the closed curve of minimum length passing through the midpoint *M* of the base of a given rectangle and dividing the area *A* of the rectangle into two simply connected parts? It is to be understood that the curve may touch the edges of the rectangle but must not wander outside its boundaries. The altitude from *M* will not do because it is not a closed curve; yet it seems that the problem ought to be solvable.

Figure 3(a) shows a closed curve through *M* dividing *A* into two parts such that the shaded area is certainly larger than the white area; in Figure 3(b) the shaded area is the smaller of the two. There are many curves which make the two areas equal. Of them, which one is the shortest? It turns out that the best curve is the circle through *M*, tangent to the base, with area equal to ½*A*. But this means that if the

[3a]

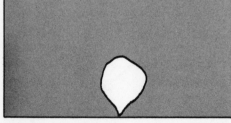

M

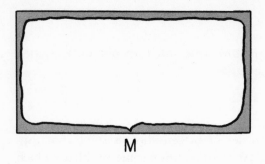

M                                    [3b]

ratio of length to breadth of the rectangle ex-
ceeds $\pi/2$, the problem has no solution: the
required circle will not fit inside the rectangle,
some other curve must be used, and there is
no shortest one.

Thirty years ago Kurt Gödel startled the
mathematical world by producing a new kind
of unsolved problem. It had always been taken
for granted (again that dangerous assumption!) that all mathematical propositions could
be proven to be either true or false. What
Gödel did, in effect, was to show that there exist
mathematical propositions which make perfectly good sense and which may be true or
may be false (in the mathematical sense of
compatible with or not compatible with a set
of stated assumptions), but for which there is
no way of ever finding out whether they are
true or false. A problem of this kind is *undecidable,* in that one cannot say whether it has
a solution or not. Many mathematicians believe that problems unsolvable in the Gödel
sense are not of frequent occurrence nor easily
stated. It seems possible that none of the prob-

lems in this book will turn out to be Gödel-undecidable.

□

Our order of presentation is somewhat random. We shall mention some problems which can be stated and understood with a minimum of mathematical background, and move from them toward problems which cannot be adequately explained without some previous mathematics, which we shall attempt to supply as needed, at least in skeletal form.

# 2

## Applied problems

We begin with a few problems which can be labeled "practical." Just how practical they are depends on the point of view; at least they can be related in some direct way to everyday life, and hence if we wish we can categorize them as among the problems of applied mathematics.

Formerly a country stationed its defensive troops in strategic positions along its border. Today, since attack has become three dimensional, one has to anticipate bombings and paratroop landings within the interior of the country. The problem of *dispersal* has therefore become one of major importance. How should one's defenses be distributed?

To simplify the problem, suppose a country with a large land area and a small population anticipates an air invasion; planes can land anywhere; there is no one spot more likely to be selected by the enemy than any other. The home army has a limited number of mobile defense units. How should they be deployed around the countryside? The enemy will find out where they are located and will land at the point whose distance from the nearest station is greatest. Therefore the object of the defenders is to select stations in that pattern which renders the greatest distance from any one point to some station a minimum. We shall call this the pattern of *best dispersal*.

The problem of best dispersal is far from completely solved. Even the answer to this simpler question is unknown: What is the best dispersal of $n$ stations (points) on a plane circular disk? More precisely, no point of the disk is at a distance greater than $k$ from some one of the stations; what is the smallest possible value of $k$ for various $n$? The answer is known for $n \leqslant 5$, but there are many values of $n > 5$ for which the smallest $k$ is not known, and a general solution seems remote at present.

On a sphere the problem becomes somewhat more interesting if we change it slightly and ask for the best *scattering* of $n$ points; that is, the arrangement which makes the least distance between any two *of them* a maximum. The dispersal problem asks how best to guard the area with stations; the scattering problem asks how best to keep the stations apart, like

Applied problems

(perhaps) an equilibrium pattern for mutually repellent particles. This may sound like two ways of saying the same thing, but it is not. One might guess that $n$ points could always be scattered on the sphere more sparsely than $n + 1$ points, but the guess is incorrect. It is not possible to scatter five points so that every pair of them is separated by more than 90° of arc. In other words, 90° is the optimum mutual separation. Yet the same statement is true of six points, which highlights the difference between dispersal and scattering. Even on a sphere, which could be considered a country with no border, the value of $k$ in the dispersal problem is not the same for $n = 5$ as it is for $n = 6$.

The values of $n$ for which the scattering problem on the sphere has been solved are 2 through 9, 11, 12, and 24. Solutions for other values of $n$, or some form of general solution, are unknown. Interestingly, the solution (recently discovered) for $n = 11$ is that there is no improvement over $n = 12$; the situation parallels the 5, 6 case.

These problems, previously thought to be of only theoretical interest, have recently acquired new practical aspects. (1) If one wishes to monitor outer space, either from one country or from the whole globe, what is the best arrangement of the listening posts (radio telescopes)? (2) The communications industry is interested in placing a large number of echo satellites into orbit for the purpose of reflecting or retransmitting line-of-sight radio waves. If these are randomly scattered, what will be their expected average separation at any instant? Is there any optimum arrangement of the orbits? (3) In the event that, some day, the reflector satellites could be replaced by space stations under their own power, which could each be held over a specified spot on the surface of the earth, what would then be the best network of such stations?

How should three cowboys, who have to watch over cattle on a square range, station themselves? This is readily recognizable as the dispersal problem for a square area with $n = 3$. Hugo Steinhaus has elaborated the problem by imposing additional intriguing restrictions. First he points out that dividing the square into three equal rectangles with a cowboy at the center of each rectangle (Figure 4) has four *advantages:* (1) The areas are equal. (2) The maximum rides (distance each cowboy has to go to reach the farthest point in his area) are equal. (3) Each point in the range is entrusted to the nearest cowboy. (4) Each

[4]

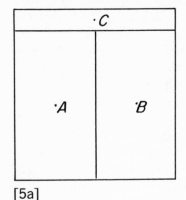

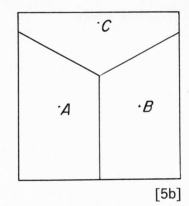

[5a]                                                    [5b]

cowboy is stationed at the point in his area
which minimizes his maximum ride. He next
considers five other partitions of the range,
each of which reduces the maximum ride but
fails to have at least one of the four advantages.
Finally he poses the question, of all those partitions possessing all four advantages, are there
any with a shorter maximum ride than that of
Figure 4?

It has recently been shown that the solution
of the unadorned dispersal problem is $k = \sqrt{65}/16$ for the unit square. Figure 5 (a and
b) shows two possible partitions with this value
of $k$. The first fails to meet advantage (3), and
both violate advantage (1). This suggests that
if the answer to the Steinhaus question is yes,
then the maximum ride for any partition which
answers it may turn out to be greater than
$\sqrt{65}/16$.

☐

What course should a ship steer in order to meet a second ship as quickly as possible? The courses of both ships are to be straight, and the first ship (pursuer) is assumed to be faster than the second ship (quarry), but both are to maintain constant course and speed. The solution for the problem thus simplified is well known. Let $P$ and $Q$ be the positions of pursuer and quarry respectively at the instant when pursuit begins. If the quarry steers any straight course, the pursuer can intercept soonest by steering another straight course aimed at the point where the fugitive's course intersects an Apollonian circle associated with $P$ and $Q$. This circle is the locus of points $k$ times as far from $P$ as from $Q$, where $k$ is the ratio of the ships' velocities (Figure 6). Note that $Q$ is not the center of the circle.

The above solution is applicable only to a plane ocean, and hence is practical for short interceptions. If the plane theory is adapted to the surface of a sphere, interception will not in general occur. To identify or characterize

[6]

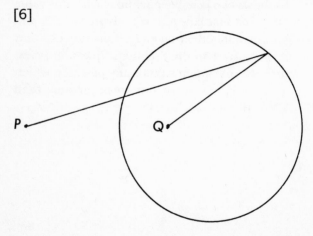

the locus of collision points on a sphere for constant speeds and great circle courses remains an unsolved problem. It may find application in long-range, high-speed air navigation where the earth's sphericity cannot be neglected.

□

A man falls overboard from a boat in a thick fog, into a wide river with parallel banks which he cannot see. He knows the width of the river but not his distance from either shore. What is his best procedure? Under the somewhat unrealistic assumption that he is able to navigate—that is, to keep track of his course—what is the shortest course he can swim and be sure of reaching land?

Another problem is posed by the boat lost at sea at a known distance but unknown direction from the nearest shore, which is this time a single straight beach. This could happen to a careless fisherman who has run out to sea a known number of miles and stopped to fish; while he is busy netting a big one, the fog settles down, so that when he is ready to go home he realizes that he has completely lost his bearings. We have to assume that he is without a reliable compass, else he would not be truly lost; still, we must stipulate that he can somehow navigate, and we ask the same question that we asked in the swimmer's problem.

The conditions are altered in a quite different version: the boat has only a limited supply of gasoline, not enough to reach shore by the answer to the previous problem under "worst possible" luck, but ample to reach shore in a straight line if the boat happens to start out in the right or nearly the right direction. What now is the best plan? That is, what course should be pursued in order to maximize the probability of reaching land before the gas gives out?

If the man in the boat miscalculates in his attempt to solve the preceding problem, the fog will eventually lift to reveal a very lonely boat, far out at sea. Somebody, we hope, will then organize a search; and immediately we have another problem on our hands. Philip M. Morse, director of the Massachusetts Institute of Technology Computation Center, has ably described the difficulties involved in what he calls a "basic search" for a ship lost on the surface of the ocean.

"We may know something as to its whereabouts and motion, which can be expressed in terms of a probability distribution—it is more likely to be here than there—for instance. We wish to distribute our search effort—the tracks of our search planes—so as to discover the ship with the least effort—the smallest number of flying hours—or we may wish to maximize our chance of discovery for a given amount of effort. Geometrically it is a question of placing a band, representing the search track of the plane, with its range of visibility, on the sea's surface so that the band covers the most likely locations of the searched-for target.

"I think you will agree that this is not a simple problem; you can probably see that the classical calculus of variations has very little to contribute to its solution. Boundary conditions of an unfamiliar sort intrude. An essential part of the problem is the continuity of the search band—the plane must fly a continuous track. It is not clear whether the answer to the two problems mentioned, discovery for minimal expected effort or optimal chance of discovery for a given length of track, are always the same. Indeed, when the estimated probability of location of the target has several peaks, representing regions where the target is more likely to be, it is not certain that a solution is always unique. And, when one adds estimates of probable motion of the target, algorithms for obtaining usable solutions are practically non-existent."

☐

While on the subject of boats we insert a problem of a very different nature drawn from the world of sport.

The rules of the International Star Class Yacht Racing Association state that a series of races shall be scored by totaling the points of each boat in each race; that in each race a boat receives one point for finishing and one point for each boat defeated; and that a tie shall be resolved in favor of the boat that has beaten the other the greatest number of times. Assuming that there are no dead-heat finishes, find the conditions under which there can be an $n$-way, unresolvable tie in an $m$-boat series of $r$ races.

By an *unresolvable* tie it meant a tie that remains even after the application of the above rule. Example: in a three-race series, A defeats B twice, B defeats C twice, C defeats A twice, and all three happen to amass the same total points. This is entirely possible, and in fact it has occurred several times in recent years in actual series of races.

(1) If $n = r$ there can always be an unresolvable tie, provided at least $n$ boats are racing. Take the order of finish of any $n$ boats in the first race; let each advance one position cyclically, so that the first goes to last place among the $n$; repeat this process for each race, and the result will be an $n$-way, unresolvable tie.

(2) If $r = 2$ there can always be up to an $m$-way, unresolvable tie: simply let the order of finish be reversed in the second race.

Both these examples illustrate *symmetric* ties, in which each tied boat beats each other tied boat the same number of times. But it is per-

Applied problems

fectly possible to have an *asymmetric* tie, provided there are enough other boats racing. Example (3) shows a three-way asymmetric tie in a five-race series of five or more boats. A beats B four times, B beats C three times, and C beats A three times. The tie is not resolved in favor of A because, under the rule, C has beaten A.

(3)

| | Daily points | | | | | Total |
|---|---|---|---|---|---|---|
| A: | 3 | 3 | 2 | 2 | 1 | 11 |
| B: | 2 | 2 | 1 | 1 | 5 | 11 |
| C: | 1 | 1 | 3 | 3 | 3 | 11 |

It appears that there must be at least five boats racing in order for B to make up the minimum deficit of four defeats, but even this is not proven. It may be possible to arrange it some other way, with only four boats. If there are seven races, four boats are certainly enough:

(4)

| | Daily points | | | | | | | Total |
|---|---|---|---|---|---|---|---|---|
| A: | 3 | 3 | 3 | 2 | 2 | 1 | 1 | 15 |
| B: | 2 | 2 | 2 | 1 | 1 | 4 | 3 | 15 |
| C: | 1 | 1 | 1 | 3 | 4 | 3 | 2 | 15 |

If *r* is composite (6, 9, etc.) the regatta can be decomposed into its prime factors for part of the answer. For instance if there are nine races there can be a three-way tie without auxiliary boats, because each of the three could repeat twice more the situation of example (1). In practice one seldom sails more than seven races in any series that is scored in this fashion, so that for higher values of $r$ the interest is theoretical. The general theory has not been explored.

A somewhat similar problem is encountered in making up a round-robin tournament schedule. J. E. Freund has presented a "simple way of constructing round robin schedules for any number of teams." The problem becomes more complicated, however, when an additional condition is imposed. Suppose a partnership is defined as a pair consisting of a man and a woman. Can two teams of eight partnerships play at eight bridge tables so that each person plays with new opponents *and* a new partner each time? Freund's treatment does not consider this version.

□

A traveling salesman wishes to start from Washington, D.C., visit every state capital in turn, and return to Washington. How should he plan his intinerary to make the trip as short as possible? One might suggest programming the problem for a computer; then let the machine calculate the lengths of all possible trips and simply select the shortest. But for the continental United States there are 48! (meaning 48 × 47 × 46 × · · · × 2 × 1) possible routes, too many for even a large computer to consider one by one. There is still no general way to solve the traveling salesman problem for an arbitrary number of cities on any map, although "a good many mathematicians have wrestled [with it] for more than twenty years."

☐

The design of an electrical switching circuit can be elegantly represented by a special kind of simple mathematical equation. The required Boolean algebra is explained in elementary language in the reference in the notes. The type of problem involved is illustrated by the following example. We wish to design a circuit connecting Terminal No. 1 with Terminal No. 2. Let A refer to all switches of type a, B to all switches of type b, and so on. Current is to flow if D is closed, provided also at least one of A, B, or C is closed; and also if D is open, provided *all* of A, B, and C are closed; but not otherwise.

One way to design the network is shown in Figure 7(a); but the conditions are also fulfilled

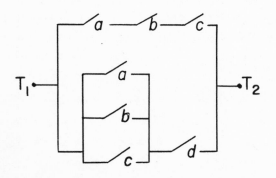

[7a]

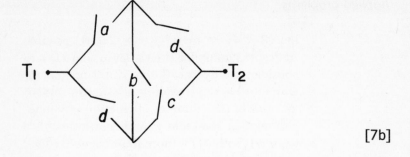

[7b]

by the so-called bridge circuit of Figure 7(b), with two fewer switches. As well as requiring less "hardware," a circuit without unnecessary switches has other important practical advantages. The problem of minimal, or most economical, network design leads to many unanswered questions. Some of these are: (1) Is there a general way of designing a switching circuit satisfying given requirements and employing a minimum number of switches? At present there is no known way, other than trial and error, of knowing whether you have hit upon the circuit that cannot be further improved. (2) The same question using series-parallel systems only (no bridges). (3) The same question when there are certain on-off combinations which never actually occur in the use of the network. (4) Is there any way of predicting whether a minimal circuit for a given problem is going to be of bridge type or series-parallel or mixed?

□

A remarkable discovery of communication theory is Shannon's Theorem, which says, in substance, that the effective capacity of a receiver increases as the volume of transmission increases, even when the "noise" (interference, errors, etc.) increases also. One might have guessed that as transmission efforts (and noise) increased indefinitely, the amount of usable reception would remain constant or decrease. It turns out not to be so.

To see what this means, imagine that we are trying to convey a message by shouting it across a river which is so wide that only scattered bits of the message come through. One way to improve reception would be to have the message repeated again and again. Reliability would then go up, because one could obtain an increasingly accurate picture of the original message by averaging out the errors of the various single attempts. But the total transmission *rate* would decrease drastically because the "line" would be tied up too long with each message. An alternative procedure would be to increase the capacity of the system as follows. Suppose we were able to find ten couples, all of different nationalities, each speaking and understanding only one language. That is, Mr. and Mrs. A. speak only Andalusian, Mr. and Mrs. B. speak only Bratislavian, and so on. Station the men on one side of the river and the women on the other. Let all the men shout the message once, simultaneously, each in his own language, and let each wife receive as much as she can of her husband's message despite the prevailing din. Shannon's Theorem states that more total message could then be reassembled by the receiving center than if only a single message were called; and that if twenty transmitters and twenty receivers operated in this fashion, the net result would be better still.

The communications industry has not succeeded in working out a practical application of Shannon's Theorem. That is, its actual implementation in terms of wires, transmitters, coding, etc., has yet to be developed. The problem has obvious economic importance in these days of overcrowded communications networks.

□

Despite the best efforts of many of the greatest mathematicians of the past two centuries, a satisfactory theory of the motions of the moon has eluded everyone. The intrinsic difficulty of the problem has led to its virtual abandonment, astronomers being content instead to rely on numerical methods which can make accurate predictions for a limited time. But the problem has taken on new significance in the calculation of orbits of man-launched or artificial satellites; and in this form, still unsolved, it demands increased attention.

□

Money deposited in U.S. Postal Savings draws interest of ½ % quarterly, beginning with the month following that in which deposited. Interest is not compounded, and is not paid until the deposit is withdrawn. Under the simplifying assumption that deposits and withdrawals are permissible in any amount whatever, find the optimum pattern of withdrawal and redeposit for an initial deposit $A$, principal and interest to be permanently withdrawn at the end of $n$ months.

□

Whoever set up the schedule of U.S. parcel post or fourth-class mail rates must have done so after a bad nightmare. There seems to be little rhyme or reason in the scheme. Robert E. Gaskell, a professional mathematician in the applied field, has suggested an amusing problem without much practical worth: Is there any formula which describes or even approximates the rule-of-thumb rates? He gave me a formula in 1959 which is already out of date because the postage rates change so frequently. At that time he claimed that it represented the required postage with an error of not more than one cent, in the weight range of any reasonable package. $N$ is the zone number, $w$ is the weight to the nearest pound, and $C$ is the cost in cents.

$$C = \frac{48 + 9n - n^2 + w(n^2 - n + 16)}{4}$$

# Tomorrow's math

In case anyone would like to while away some idle hours trying to bring the formula up to date or deriving a better one, here are the parcel post rates as listed in the 1962 *World Almanac*.

| Zone Number | Base rate (1 to 2 lb.) | Each additional pound |
|---|---|---|
| Local | 24¢ | 2¢ |
| 1, 2 | 33¢ | 5¢ to 10 lb., then 4¢ |
| 3 | 35¢ | 6¢ to 15 lb., then 5¢ |
| 4 | 39¢ | 8¢ to 5 lb., 7¢ 6 to 50 lb., then 6¢ |
| 5 | 45¢ | 10¢ to 20 lb., 9¢ 21 to 50 lb., then 8¢ |
| 6 | 51¢ | 13¢ to 10 lb., 12¢ 11 to 30 lb., then 11¢ |
| 7 | 58¢ | 16¢ to 15 lb., 15¢ 16 to 30 lb., 14¢ 31 to 50 lb., then 13¢ |
| 8 | 64¢ | 19¢ to 10 lb., 18¢ 11 to 30 lb., 17¢ 31 to 40 lb., then 16¢ |

These are domestic rates only. I do not dare to suggest trying to include the overseas rates in the same formula.

☐

In the past, on college campuses where the fraternity system flourished, it was customary to allow each fraternity to choose more or less freely whom it should invite to become members. There were rules and "codes of rushing," but even so some inequities were bound to occur, and many undergraduates never had a chance to get into any fraternity. In an attempt to modernize the system, several colleges have recently instituted "total opportunity" schemes, whereby each student has at least the option of joining some fraternity if he wishes to. After the fraternities look over the candidates and vice versa, the fraternities submit lists of names and the students indicate their order of preference to a central committee. "Rushing" takes place according to a highly organized and rigid procedure designed to produce a maximum of suitable fits and a minimum of disappointing misfits. It is clear that some rather complicated mathematics is involved in designing an adequate system. Disregarding the difficulties due to human frailties and fickleness, not even the theoretical part of the problem is completely solved.

Almost the same problem is encountered by

the college admissions offices in their attempts
to select suitable freshman classes from among
the eligible applicants. To date no central or
national co-ordinating bureau of admissions
exists, partly because no one has offered a
convincing mathematical solution of the problem. Only very recently an attack has been
made indicating that a realistic solution is by
no means unattainable.

# 3

# Problems concerning games

Because of the mathematical structure of some games, interesting problems arise or can be invented around them. We look into a few of these, and then conclude the chapter with a brief mention of the new field of mathematics called Game Theory.

Stanislav M. Ulam, whose problems usually contain an added dimension of difficulty when compared with others of the same kind, offers this stiff one in the game of bridge. Does there exist a possible deal with the following properties? (1) North and South can make against any defense a grand slam in *any* suit provided that suit is trump; but (2) against good defense they can make only five no-trump. Ulam believes that they can always make at least five (that is, a total of eleven tricks); the question is, can they always make at least six? He has devised a hand with property (1) in which they cannot make seven.

☐

This chess problem was given to me by Martin Gardner, who says it is an old favorite but still unsolved. From the sixteen black pieces, remove the eight pawns, and place the remaining black pieces on the board in such a way that every space, including the occupied ones, is challenged by at least one piece. The two bishops must go on opposite colors, just as in actual play. It is not difficult to challenge sixty-three squares in this way; whether all sixty-four can be "covered" is not known.

☐

The next problem is a paradox.

The headmaster of a school announced that some afternoon during the following week, on one of the weekdays Monday through Saturday, inclusive, there would be a surprise examination in a certain subject. The exact day of the exam was to be kept secret from the students, because if they knew which afternoon it was to be, they could do some last minute cramming in the morning, and this the headmaster wished to prevent. He made it a sporting proposition by promising (and we are to assume that a headmaster's promise is binding), that if any student came to him during some morning and told him that the exam was to be given that day, and supplied him with a rational explanation leading to this conclusion, then he would cancel the exam, since it would no longer be a surprise.

The students got together over the weekend and came up with a brilliant idea. They nominated Algernon to present it to the headmaster on Monday morning.

"Sir," said Algy, "I am happy to inform you —I mean I am afraid you cannot give us that exam at all."

"No?"

"Will you agree that it would not be a surprise if you saved it until Saturday? Surely if we had not yet had the exam, we would know on Saturday morning that it must come that afternoon, since it would be the only day left. One of us would come and tell you so, and you would have to cancel it."

"Very true. I cannot use Saturday, for the reason you give."

"So we may as well cross Saturday off the calendar? It is no longer an available day."

Reluctantly, seeing which way the argument was leading him, the headmaster had to agree.

"Very good," said Algy. "The week, effectively, starts on Monday and ends on Friday. But the very fact that you cannot use Saturday for the exam renders Friday useless also.

For on Friday morning, not yet having had the examination, we would have to expect it on Friday afternoon. Thus Friday's exam could not be a surprise, and must be cancelled. So Friday must be crossed off the calender too."

"You need say no more," said the headmaster, in deep perpelexity. "I see that you can carry the argument back through the week, rendering each day unusable. It appears that no surprise exam is possible."

Algernon reported triumphantly to his colleagues that it had all worked out exactly as they had figured it must.

The paradox, however, is this. Although the above logic seems unassailable, what is to prevent the headmaster from selecting in advance some day at random, say Wednesday, which he reveals to no one? When Wednesday morning rolls around, how is any student to know that the exam will be given that afternoon? Will not all conditions for a surprise have been fulfilled? No explanation of these apparently conflicting answers has been given, although more than one learned paper has been written in an attempt to resolve the paradox.

☐

A Graeco-Latin square was originally an array made up of Greek letters and Roman letters. One can use any two distinguishable

| A 1 | B 2 | C 3 |
| B 3 | C 1 | A 2 |
| C 2 | A 3 | B 1 |

[8]

sets of *n* objects each, say letters and numbers, to form an *n* by *n* square. In each compartment of the square appears one letter and one number; but none appears twice in a single column or row. Furthermore, each number may be paired only once with each letter. Figure 8 shows a Graeco-Latin square of order 3.

Leonard Euler proved that such squares of odd order are always possible, and also of even orders divisible by 4. Graeco-Latin squares of even orders not divisible by 4 (6, 10, 14, etc.) he conjectured to be impossible. It is true that one cannot construct such a square of order 2 or 6; but in 1959 it was shown that all the others are theoretically possible; and one of order 10 was actually constructed.

Instead of using a letter and a number in each compartment, we can use a first digit and a second digit, where now 4 7 does not mean forty-seven; it means the object numbered 4 from the first set and the object num-

41

| 00 | 47 | 18 | 76 | 29 | 93 | 85 | 34 | 61 | 52 |
|----|----|----|----|----|----|----|----|----|----|
| 86 | 11 | 57 | 28 | 70 | 39 | 94 | 45 | 02 | 63 |
| 95 | 80 | 22 | 67 | 38 | 71 | 49 | 56 | 13 | 04 |
| 59 | 96 | 81 | 33 | 07 | 48 | 72 | 60 | 24 | 15 |
| 73 | 69 | 90 | 82 | 44 | 17 | 58 | 01 | 35 | 26 |
| 68 | 74 | 09 | 91 | 83 | 55 | 27 | 12 | 46 | 30 |
| 37 | 08 | 75 | 19 | 92 | 84 | 66 | 23 | 50 | 41 |
| 14 | 25 | 36 | 40 | 51 | 62 | 03 | 77 | 88 | 99 |
| 21 | 32 | 43 | 54 | 65 | 06 | 10 | 89 | 97 | 78 |
| 42 | 53 | 64 | 05 | 16 | 20 | 31 | 98 | 79 | 87 |

[9]

bered 7 from the second set. The Graeco-Latin square of order 10 shown in Figure 9 is due to E. T. Parker, one of the men who first proved its possibility.

One notices that the nine squares forming the lower, right-hand corner of this array constitute a miniature Graeco-Latin square of order 3 in the two sets of symbols (7, 8, 9). In fact it is the same as the one shown in Figure 8. All squares of order 10 so far constructed have the property of containing within themselves a subsquare of order 3. Why this happens, or even whether it always happens, is not known.

□

A new idea, called the theory of polyominoes, has appeared within the last two or three years. A polyomino is to be imagined (or actually cut out of a piece of cardboard, wood, or what have you) to be made up of a certain number of squares joined along one or more edges. Figure 10 shows a tetromino, and Figure 11 two pentominoes. Of course there are many others.

The game of making patterns with these objects contains many difficult problems. For example, there exist twelve differently shaped pentominoes. A man wishes to construct a set

[10]

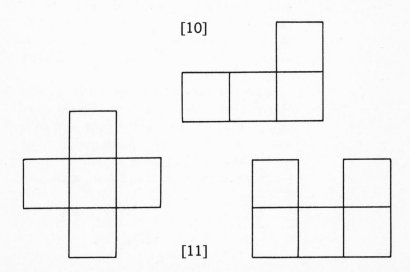

[11]

of one of each of them from a single piece of plywood, but his saw will not cut around corners. What is the smallest plywood rectangle he can buy? It is known that it can be done from a $6 \times 13$ piece; but this wastes eighteen squares, because twelve pentominoes actually occupy only sixty squares. Is there any more economical way of making the cuts?

It is known that there are 12 pentominoes 35 different hexominoes, and 108 different septominoes. But no one has succeeded in finding a general formula for the number of $n$-ominoes in terms of $n$.

□

Here is an apparently innocent programming problem which can lead to hours of investigation. What is the longest finite sequence of "one's" that can be "printed out" by three cards, each with three sets of instructions? The instructions tell what is to be done under three possible contingencies and give directions how to proceed to the next card. Also in order to make the sequence finite, one stop instruction must appear somewhere.

Refer to Figure 12, and let us look at card No. 1. The top line says if we find a blank space (B), print a one, move to the right, and go to card 2 for instructions. The second line says if we find a zero (0), erase it, print a 1 in its place, move to the left, and go to card 3 for

| Card 1 | | | Card 2 | | | Card 3 | |
|---|---|---|---|---|---|---|---|
| B | 1–R–2 | | B | 1–L–2 | | B | 1–L–3 |
| 0 | 1–L–3 | | 0 | 1–L–1 | | 0 | 1–L–3 |
| 1 | B–R–2 | | 1 | 0–R–1 | | 1 | 1–R–STOP |

[12]

instructions. The third line says if we find a one (1), print a blank (that is, erase the 1 and put nothing in its place), move to the right, and go to card 2 for instructions.

Suppose now we start our "machine" by feeding in the three cards of Figure 12 so that it first "reads" card 1. We have nothing on the output, so all spaces are blank, and hence it takes the instruction opposite B, which is to print 1, move one space to the right, and go to card 2 for instructions. The output register now looks like this, where we purposely did not start at the left-hand end in case an instruction asked us to go to the left:

| | | 1 | | | | | | | |
|---|---|---|---|---|---|---|---|---|---|

When we have moved to the right we again encounter a blank, for which card 2 says to print a 1, move to the left, and go to card 2 for instructions:

| | | 1 | 1 | | | | | | |
|---|---|---|---|---|---|---|---|---|---|

On card 2 opposite "1" it says erase, print a zero, move to the right, and go to card 1 for instructions. Instead of erasing, we wish to keep a record of all operations, so we put a line through the 1 and write the new 0 beneath:

| | | ~~1~~ | 1 | | | | | | |
|---|---|---|---|---|---|---|---|---|---|
| | | 0 | | | | | | | |

Card 1 says when you find a "1", erase, move to the right, and go to card 2 for instructions:

| | | ~~1~~ | ~~1~~ | | | | | | |
|---|---|---|---|---|---|---|---|---|---|
| | | 0 | | | | | | | |

You should now be able to continue the routine yourself. The sequence will finally lead you to the last line of card 3, after which the completed print-out will be the contents of the bottom squares of all columns:

| | ~~1~~ | ~~1~~ | ~~1~~ | ~~1~~ | ~~1~~ | ~~1~~ | 1 | | |
|---|---|---|---|---|---|---|---|---|---|
| | 1 | ~~0~~ | ~~1~~ | ~~0~~ | ~~0~~ | 1 | | | |
| | | ~~1~~ | 1 | 1 | 1 | | | | |
| | | ~~0~~ | | | | | | | |
| | | 1 | | | | | | | |

The original problem was to design a program which would print out the sequence of 1's of maximum possible length. Tibor Rado, who invented the game, would like to know of any three-card program (of this type) which will produce a string of 1's longer than seven. Very little is known of any theory connected with the problem. It is entertaining yet perplexing and probably fundamental mathematics.

□

A weighing problem which has been going the rounds of some mathematical communities is the problem of the balls. Given $n$ distinguishable balls, of which it is known that no two have the same weight, it is required that they be arranged in order of magnitude by weighings of one against one in a pan balance scale (no weights). What is the smallest number of weighings, as a function of $n$, which will always suffice? What strategy (procedure) does one adopt to achieve this minimum? Some assortments (depending on luck) will be more quickly ordered than others. Will the best strategy automatically minimize the *expected* number of weighings, if the original ordering is random?

"The Theory of Games is a method of analyzing a conflict, according to the following abstraction: The conflict is a situation in which there are two sets of opposing interests; it may be regarded as a game between two players, each of whom represents one set of interests. Each player has a finite set of strategies from which he may, on any given play of the game, choose one. The total assets of the players are the same at the end of any one play of the game as at the beginning." Of course some of them have changed hands, from one player to the other; but no assets have leaked away, evaporated, or been paid to the house. "Each player wishes to pursue a conservative plan which will maximize his average gains; these maximum average gains, called the value of the game, may be calculated. Each player can, through proper play, be sure that he will receive the value of the game; to ensure this, he must choose his strategy properly—and a method exists for deciding which strategy to choose."

A strategy means a fixed procedure which one player adopts against the opponent or nature or chance or whatever device the "other player" can be considered to be. John von Neumann, who virtually invented game theory, has discussed thoroughly the theory of two-person, finite, zero-sum games. Sometimes there is no single best strategy; but von Neumann's main theorem is that in all simple two-person games there always exists a certain *mixed* strategy which is optimal. That is, one sometimes plays one way and sometimes another, in certain definite ascertainable proportions.

Game theory is a new and little-explored field, with many applications. Much work remains to be done. Although two-person games have been investigated, practically nothing is known of the theory of $n$-person games where $n = 3$ or more.

# 4

## Geometrical problems

There exists a large class of pure geometry problems of which the following is a typical example.

"In a tetrahedron $ABCD$ let $L$ be the second Lemoine point (i.e. the point whose distances from the planes of the faces are proportional to the circumradii of these faces) and let $L'$, $L''$, $L'''$ be the harmonic conjugates of $L$ with respect to the points where lines through $L$ cut the edges $BC$ and $DA$, $CA$ and $DB$, $AB$ and $DC$. Show (1) the tetrahedron $LL'L''L'''$ is self-conjugate with respect to the sphere $ABCD$; (2) the polar planes of $L$, $L'$, $L''$, $L'''$ with respect to the sphere $ABCD$ coincide with the polar planes of these points with respect to the tetrahedron $ABCD$."

It would take considerable effort and a

lengthy discussion simply to lay the ground-work necessary to understand the problem. There is a small group of enthusiasts who still delight in this field of pure synthetic geometry; but it is an indoor sport which was more popular in the nineteenth century than it is today.

A somewhat different kind of problem is the following. "Consider a parabola having its vertex at a variable point $M$ on a given plane curve, and its focus at $F$, the point dividing the radius of curvature $MC$ in a constant ratio; the parabola touches its complete enve-lope at $M$ and also at two other finite points. The corresponding chord of contact is perpen-dicular to the line joining $M$ to the midpoint of the radius of curvature at $C$ of the evolute of the given curve. If this chord of contact intersects $MF$ at $D$, then $DC = MF$." The problem is to prove these statements. At last report (1957) both this and the preceding problem remained unsolved.

This one is probably best attacked by ana-lytic methods, removing the "pure geometry" objection if it is an objection. But you have doubtless already sensed another weakness. The problem describes an intricate set of con-ditions which, if fulfilled, produce an extremely specialized result that does not seem worth the top-heavy structure of the requirements. One doubts whether it could be extended or generalized. It is perhaps unfair to judge a problem without first solving it and thus discovering its inner beauty; history has many times shown the rashness of prejudging the worth of any mathematical offering. But without further apology we shall leave these two problems and move on to some others that have either the advantage of greater simplicity or the attraction of wider application.

☐

Modern geometers concern themselves with many topics never mentioned in high school, representing an entirely different approach (and category of difficulty) from that of classical Euclidean geometry. You might have trouble recognizing some of these topics as geometry at all. The concept of *least covering area* yields some very ticklish questions. Here is a long-standing problem credited to Lebesgue: What is the size and shape of the least area that will cover (in the sense of a sheet of paper) any arbitrary area or point-set in the plane the maximum distance between any two points of which is 1? The covered figure can measure not more than 1 in any direction; the covering figure must be able to cover *any* such.

The circle of diameter 1 will not do the trick. Figure 13 shows an area bounded by three circular arcs of radius 1, one of the *curves of constant width* which are not themselves circles. No two of its points are separated by a distance greater than 1; but the circle fails to cover it. The closest approximation to date seems to be the area of Figure 14. One starts with the regular hexagon which circumscribes the circle of diameter 1 and snips from it three of the corners as indicated. Information on the problem is scanty.

Leo Moser, of the University of Alberta, asks another question concerning minimal covering. Any number of squares whose total area equals one square unit may be moved about and packed together in the plane, but no overlapping is to be allowed. Supposing them to be packed as closely as possible, under the worst conditions of size and number of squares what is the smallest covering square? That is, how big a square must we use to be sure to be able to cover the given squares provided they are judiciously packed? The prob-

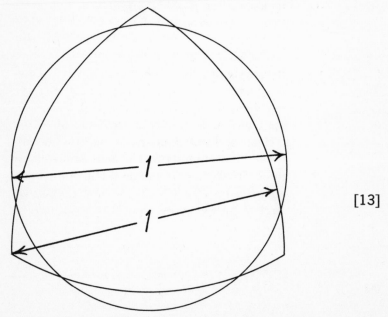

[13]

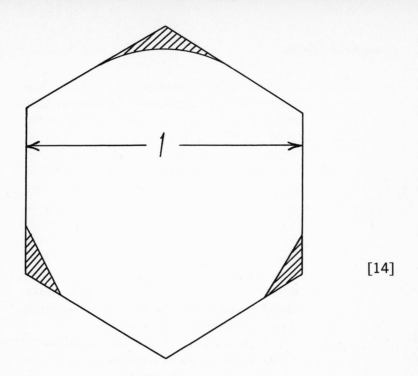

lem is slippery because of the three parameters: number of squares, size of each square, position of squares. The controls are: total area equals one unit, individual shapes are square, covering area is square.

□

The maximum distance between any two points of a plane figure is called its *diameter*. What is the plane figure of least area with a given circumference and diameter? This is a question from the theory of convex bodies, a subject in which even the elementary theory turns out to be unexpectedly intricate. A close alliance with the analytical theory of inequalities invests the topic with added interest. We shall describe a few more of its unsolved problems.

Given a plane convex figure $F$ with two perpendicular chords that cut its perimeter into four equal parts, then twice the sum of the lengths of the chords is thought to be at least equal to the perimeter of $F$. Equality holds only for rectangles, which are not strictly convex figures. Another guess about this same figure is that the sum of the lengths of the chords is at least the diameter of $F$. Neither of these conjectures has been proven.

A circle is a plane curve such that all chords through a given fixed point (in this case the center) have the same length. This property, however, does not characterize a circle: there are other convex curves with the same property. It is not known whether there exists a plane curve, convex or otherwise, such that two points, $A$ and $B$, both have the equichordal property; that is, all chords through $A$ or $B$ are equal.

Suppose we have a given convex body in ordinary Euclidean 3-space and an arbitrary point $O$ in its interior. Consider the point $P$ defined as follows: the length of the segment $OP$ is equal to the area of the plane section of the convex body through $O$ and perpendicular to $OP$. As the plane section takes all possible positions through $O$, does the point $P$ sweep out a second convex surface?

A homogeneous solid cylindrical rod whose cross section is a circle has floating equilibrium (if it is light enough to float at all) in any position; that is, no matter how we turn it around its axis, it will remain at rest on the surface of the water in that position. H. Auerbach has found curves other than circles with this property. Hugo Steinhaus, in commenting on such curves, says that "they are so calculated that every chord halving the circumference also halves the area. Hence this property is not peculiar to the circle." The juxtaposition of these statements is confusing: it is not clear what "this property" refers to. The second property, that every chord halving the circumference also halves the area, is so obviously not peculiar to the circle that it scarcely seems worth while to mention it. For instance, every rectangle has the property. Yet that property is certainly not the one that gives the body floating equilibrium in any position. An ordinary plank, whose cross section is a rectangle, has only two equilibrium positions. The physical requirement for floating equilibrium is that the center of gravity of the submerged portion be in the same vertical line as the center of gravity of the whole body.

In three dimensions the problem is still unsolved. If a convex body floats in equilibrium in any orientation, it is necessarily a sphere?

There are associated problems. H. T. Croft suggests this procedure: Denote plane sections of a convex body as follows:

V: those that cut off a certain constant volume;

P: those whose section has a certain constant area;

S: those that cut off a certain constant surface area of the body;

T: those making a constant angle with the tangent planes to the body at all points of the boundary.

Then ask questions by pairing letters; for instance, one could ask, if all sections of type V are also of type S, is the body necessarily a sphere? I do not know which, if any, have been answered.

Some investigations have been made of the theory of inscribed plane figures which can be rotated freely in a circumscribing polygon while remaining in contact with every side of the polygon. There are infinitely many curves which are not circles but which can be rotated inside a regular polygon of $n$ sides while always remaining in contact with the sides. If $n$ is greater than 4, it is not known which of these curves bounds the least area. Such questions, which seem very abstract, sometimes have application to problems in mechanics.

In many specialized fields there are men who make a hobby, or perhaps even a lifework, of some particular portion of the topic, ultimately becoming world authorities on their chosen subject. On the curves described in the last paragraph, such a man is Michael Goldberg, head engineer of the U.S. Navy Department's Bureau of Ordnance. He calls them rotors; in a 1957 paper he conjectured the kind of rotor required to solve the aforementioned problem. In another place he asks, "Are there non-spherical shapes which can be rotated through all orientations while remaining in contact with the three faces of a regular triangular prism?"

For a convex curve, there always exist three concurrent chords bisecting each other and intersecting at angles of 60°. Steinhaus, who proved this, believes it to be true for any simple closed curve, whether convex or not, but he has been unable to prove it.

It is impossible to bend a closed convex surface, a fact exploited by nature in the design of birds' eggs, whose shells would have to be far heavier if the egg had any other shape. When a ping-pong ball is dented, some tearing or stretching of the surface actually takes place. If an arbitrarily small hole is cut out of a convex surface, the surface can then be bent. It is not known whether it is sufficient merely to slit the surface, or whether even the removal of some isolated points would make it bendable.

Every closed convex polyhedron is also rigid. But according to Hilbert and Cohn-Vossen, there exist closed non-convex (i.e. re-entrant) polyhedra whose faces can be moved relative to each other. What is not known is whether, under such a motion, the volume changes.

☐

The following question is asked by Leo Moser. What is the least number of colors with which one can color a plane map in such a way that no two points one unit apart are ever the same color? That seven colors suffice is demonstrated in Figure 15. The pattern can be extended. Each number represents a different color, and the diameter of each hexagon is slightly less than 1, say 0.99. The question is, are seven colors necessary, and if not, what is the minimum number?

A similar coloring question deals with triangles. What is the least number of colors required in order to ensure that a given equilateral triangle dropped on a map can never have all three vertices on the same color? The problem is said to be solved for plane maps but not for maps on the surface of a sphere.

☐

Two lines in the plane in general intersect in one point. The exceptional case is parallelism, when they do not intersect at all. In three dimensions the situation is somewhat reversed: two lines do not intersect (they are said to be

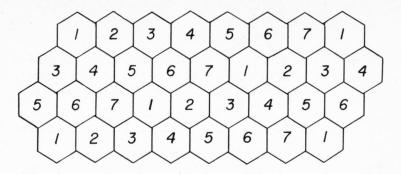

skew to each other) unless they lie in the same plane, in which case they do intersect unless they are parallel. Two skew lines have one and only one common perpendicular, the length of which measures the shortest distance, or more simply the distance, between the two lines. How many lines can be drawn in 3-space, each a unit distant from every one of the others? It is conjectured that seven is the maximum number, but no proof is available. Seven might be too high or too low.

☐

How many different distances can there be between the vertices of a convex irregular polygon? It is known that there can be $n/3$, where $n$ is the number of vertices; but Erdos conjectures that there can be as many as $n/2$.

☐

Here are two amusing but none the less difficult problems proposed by Steinhaus.

(1) Consider a billiard table whose bound-

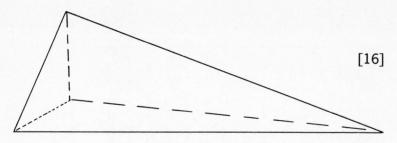

ary (cushion) has the form of a smooth convex curve. Call a triangle $ABC$ a periodic triangle if the points $A$, $B$, $C$ are such that $ABCABCABC$ ... is a possible course for a billiard ball. The triangle of maximum perimeter inscribable in the boundary is known to be one such periodic triangle. The question is, is there always at least one other one?

(2) Consider a small ball bouncing around the inside of a regular tetrahedron, not hitting the edges or vertices. If the force of gravity were neglected, would there be any periodic circuits?

☐

If one inscribes a triangle in a given triangle, the given triangle is subdivided into four smaller ones. Of these, can the inscribed triangle ever have the least perimeter? Equality occurs when the vertices of the inscribed triangle are the midpoints of the sides of the given triangle.

☐

It is fairly obvious, and it is possible to prove, that the longest line segment contained in or

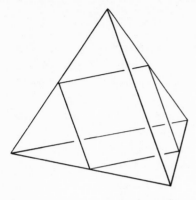

[17]

on a triangle is the longest side itself. What is not known is the extension to three dimensions: Is the maximum plane section of a triangular pyramid (tetrahedron) its largest face? (See Figure 16.) It would seem so, but one must be wary of jumping to conclusions in solid geometry. For instance it is "obvious" but entirely false that every plane section of a tetrahedron is triangular. Figure 17 shows a square cross section of a regular tetrahedron. A cube can be sliced so that the section is a regular hexagon, by a plane through the center perpendicular to a main diagonal (Figure 18). Contrary, perhaps, to expecta-

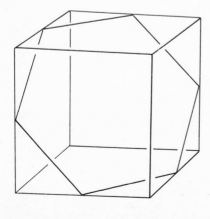

[18]

tion, such a section is not the maximum one. Alan R. Hyde has shown that the section through two opposite parallel edges has the maximum area ($\sqrt{2}$ for a unit cube).

What is the largest plane section of a solid right-circular cylinder of radius $r$ and altitude $h$? It is not, as might first be supposed, the elliptical section obtained by slicing diagonally (Figure 19). A section nearer the vertical, cutting across the ends of the cylinder, has greater area. The angle of the cutting plane for maximum area depends on the ratio of $h$ to $r$. One can set up an expression for the area as a function of this ratio and apply the maximizing device of elementary calculus; but the resulting equation is awkward and can probably be solved only by methods of approximation. A formula for the maximum area in terms of $h$ and $r$ is not at present accessible.

□

Problems of dissection owe their difficulty to the fact that they follow no apparent pattern. Every solution is different, and each problem must be handled separately.

[19]

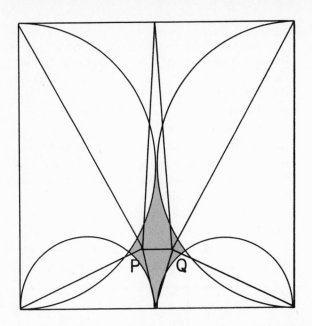

[20]

A triangle is called acute if all its angles are of less than 90°; an obtuse triangle contains one obtuse angle. It is known that an obtuse triangle can always be cut into not more than seven acute triangles, and that seven are in general necessary. Under certain known conditions on the sizes of the angles, the seven acute triangles can be isosceles. In general, an obtuse triangle can always be dissected into eight acute isosceles triangles. *Question:* Can it always be dissected into seven?

What is the smallest number of acute angled triangles necessary to dissect a square? This problem has recently been solved: eight triangles are necessary, Figure 20 showing how the cuts should be made. If points $P$ and $Q$ are taken within the shaded area, it is clear that all eight triangles are acute. That eight is indeed the minimum is said to have been proved; but whether the solution of Figure 20 is essentially unique is not known.

A square can be cut into twenty-four smaller squares all of different sizes. (See Figure 21.) Is this the least possible number, if no two squares are to be alike?

The present state of knowledge concerning various dissection problems is displayed in Figure 22. The numbers in the boxes indicate the least known number of pieces required to

[21]

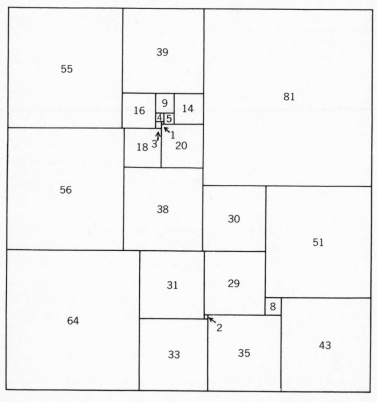

| Regular polygon of $N$ sides; $N =$ | 3 | 4 | 5 | 6 | 7 | 8 | 12 | Greek cross ✚ |
|---|---|---|---|---|---|---|---|---|
| 4 | 4 | | | | | | | |
| 5 | 6 | 6 | | | | | | |
| 6 | 5 | 5 | 7 | | | | | |
| 7 | 10 | 9 | 11 | 11 | | | | |
| 8 | 8 | 5 | 9 | 9 | 13 | | | |
| 12 | 8 | 6 | · | · | · | · | | |
| Greek cross ✚ | 5 | 4 | 7 | 7 | 12 | 9 | 6 | |
| Latin cross ✚ | 5 | 5 | 8 | 7 | 12 | 8 | 7 | 7 |

Regular polygon, No. indicates No. of sides

[22]

dissect the plane figure listed on the left and reassemble (turning pieces over if necessary) to form the indicated figure at the bottom. This table gives the current (1962) minimum figures. In nearly all cases it is not known whether these are "best possible."

□

A long-standing problem deals with the closest *packing* of spheres of equal sizes. Usually one imagines the spheres packed in a small part

of a very large container, so that border conditions are neglected. The closest packing
known has a density of 0.74; that is, nearly
three-quarters of the space is filled by the
spheres. Whether this is the densest possible is
not known; but it was proved in 1958 that if
there exists a closer packing its density cannot
exceed 0.78. This is a theoretical absolute
upper limit.

☐

We state without comment a problem which
sounds geometric but which one can hope to
solve probably only by means of set-theoretic
considerations. Show that in every neighborhood of a point on a sufficiently smooth surface there exist four points on the surface
which are the vertices of a square. The surface
$z = f(x, y)$ is "sufficiently smooth" whenever
$f(x, y)$ is continuous; or possibly it must also
have continuous first partial derivatives.

Donald Greenspan, at Purdue University,
wants to know about a simple closed curve in
Euclidean 3-space which satisfies the following two properties: (1) no three points of the
curve lie on a straight line; (2) no four points
of the curve lie on a circle. Does such a curve
exist? If so, give an example of one.

☐

If equilateral triangles are "inscribed in" an equilateral hyperbola, the locus of centroids of these triangles is another equilateral hyperbola. Are there any other curves with this property? What is the equation of the most general curve such that the locus of centroids of inscribed equilateral triangles is the same curve?

The perpendicular bisectors of the sides of a given quadrilateral $Q_1$ form a quadrilateral $Q_2$, and the perpendicular bisectors of the sides of $Q_2$ form a quadrilateral $Q_3$. Show that $Q_3$ is similar to $Q_1$, and find the ratio of simil-

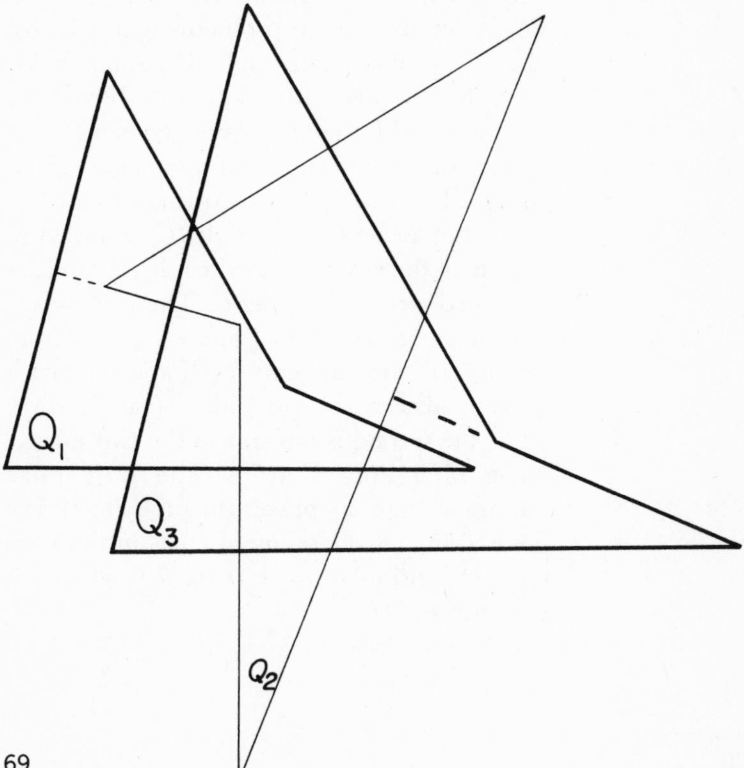

[23]

$Q_1$

$Q_3$

$Q_2$

itude. It is of course *not* sufficient to show that the sides are respectively parallel, which is trivially evident. An interesting feature is that the construction is not reversible: if you start with $Q_3$ (see Figure 23), you do not return to $Q_1$. It is easy to see why not. The sought ratio of similitude is greater than one, in the quadrilateral which we happen to have chosen; hence the new quadrilateral must always be larger than the old. In fact if the construction is iterated, continuing the same notation we observe that $Q_4$ and $Q_2$ bear the same relation as $Q_3$ and $Q_1$, and this property is general.

Our catalog of geometric questions has finally led us back to problems with which a classical geometrician would feel at home. We close this chapter with another problem from ordinary, old-fashioned plane geometry.

Through the vertex $A$ of a triangle $ABC$ a straight line $AM$ is drawn cutting the side $BC$ in $M$. Let $2\theta$ be the angle $AMC$; $O$ and $I$ the centers of the circumscribed circle $(O)$ and the inscribed circle $(I)$ of $ABC$. The circles $(\omega_1)$ and $(\omega_2)$ with centers $\omega_1$ and $\omega_2$ and radii $\rho_1$ and $\rho_2$ are each tangent to $(O)$ and the first is tangent also to the two sides of angle $AMC$ while the second is tangent to the two sides of angle $AMB$. Prove that: (1) The straight line joining $\omega_1$ and $\omega_2$ passes through $I$. (2) The point $I$ divides the segment $\omega_1\omega_2$ in the ratio $\tan^2\theta/1$; and $\rho_1 + \rho_2 = (r \sec \theta)^2$, where $r$ is the radius of $(I)$.

The problem is elementary but difficult. Part 1 can almost surely be solved by someone with sufficient ingenuity and persistence using only synthetic (Euclidean) methods. Part 2 is probably more amenable to methods of analysis and co-ordinate geometry.

This problem was proposed by Victor Thébault of Le Mans, France, and published in the American Mathematical Monthly in 1938. It is one of hundreds submitted by this most productive problemist between 1933 and 1960 when he died at the age of seventy-eight. He was adept at number theory as well as geometry. "M. Thébault's prolific output of theorems and problems about numbers is a source of constant admiration, little short of wonder, on the part of all those upon whom the higher arithmetic exerts its fascination." M. Thébault's own views are worth quoting: "Some mathematicians exhibit a tendency, not altogether free from a certain disdain, to see in such problems only insignificant trifles. Trifles, if you please, but the solution of which often demands no less penetration of mind, ingenuity, and subtle artifice than many questions of allegedly deeper significance. Moreover the study of an elementary proposition sometimes necessitates an effort which is far from negligible, which constitutes an excellent intellectual exercise, and which leads to something worthwhile indeed."

# 5

# Arithmetical problems

Number theory, sometimes called the higher arithmetic, abounds in unsolved problems of a very considerable degree of difficulty. The field represents an example of what we discussed in Chapter 1: although extremely difficult by numerical methods, some of the problems have recently been solved by embedding them in the field of analysis. Since number theory deals exclusively with the properties of *whole numbers,* the integers 1, 2, 3, 4, . . . , it was an unexpected discovery that any results at all could be obtained through methods usually reserved for *continuous* operations. In analysis one deals with variables which can take on any real value whatever, including the integers but also including all the (infinite supply of ) numbers between the integers. Most of the recent results have been obtained by analytical methods of an advanced nature and it is a reasonable hope that further progress will be made in that direction.

Perhaps the most famous unsolved problem in all of mathematics is Fermat's Last Theorem. It should be called a conjecture inasmuch as Fermat did not leave us a proof. He said he had a "wonderful" proof; and in every other case where he made such a statement a proof was subsequently found, but never for the last theorem.

The equation $x^2 + y^2 = z^2$ has many solutions, in fact an infinite number of them, in which $x$, $y$, and $z$ are all positive integers. A familiar one is $3^2 + 4^2 = 5^2$, and another is $5^2 + 12^2 = 13^2$. It is easy to write formulas producing all the solutions. In fact these formulas, or their equivalents, are rediscovered every year by vigorous amateurs. To discover something oneself is no less exciting or praiseworthy because it has been done previously by someone else.

Now consider the equation $x^n + y^n = z^n$. Fermat's Last Theorem states that this equation has no solution whatever in positive integers if $n$ is any integer greater than 2. This most surprising fact—and it does seem to be a fact, even though no general proof has yet been produced—has recently been checked for a wide range of $n$, say all $n$ less than 2000. The checking can be done by refining the problem and feeding it into a large electronic computer. Inasmuch as even a small number like 2 raised to the two-thousandth power yields a perfectly enormous integer, there is no possible chance that anyone can stumble upon a counterexample to the theorem by hand methods: there are none within reach. What remains to be done with pencil and paper and brain power is precisely that which cannot be done by any machine: to find a proof covering at once *all* cases, so that it is no longer a matter of trial and error. Fermat said he possessed such a proof. The unsuccessful search for it by hundreds of competent mathematicians over the years has led many to believe that Fermat was mistaken, that what he thought was a proof—and no one questions his sincerity— must have contained a flaw. Whether that is so or not, the search has been far from useless. From it have stemmed many other interesting results. A branch of mathematics called the theory of algebraic numbers was developed largely as a consequence of this very search.

Number theory frequently concerns itself with primes; in fact one could almost say that number theory *is* the study of prime numbers. A prime, you will recall, is a number like 5 (or 11 or 29) which has no divisors except itself and 1. A number like 15 is said to be composite: its factors are 3 and 5. Primes are special numbers, for many reasons, and we should therefore like to know all about them.

At present we know almost nothing about them. It is known that they constitute an infinite set: there is no last prime. But what are they? How can you tell by looking at a given number, say 39,617, whether it is prime or composite? How many primes are there smaller than 39,617? What is the first prime after 39,617? What is the sequence of gaps between primes? None of these questions has ever been answered.

The only known (workable) test for the primality of a number $N$ is to divide it by all the lesser primes 2, 3, 5, 7, 11, 13, . . . , up to the square root of $N$, one after the other, thus testing by sheer trial whether $N$ has a divisor. There is no need to go beyond $\sqrt{N}$; for if a larger number divided $N$, the quotient would be *less* than $\sqrt{N}$, and hence would have been found in a previous trial.

There is no known formula which generates all the primes; indeed, there is no formula which is guaranteed to produce *any* of them. Fermat thought he might have such a formula, but it is important to note that this time he confessed that he could find no proof, which is hardly surprising inasmuch as the supposed formula breaks down. Fermat found that

$$X = 2^{2^n} + 1$$

produces a value of $X$ which is a prime for the first few $n$'s. For $n = 0, 1, 2, 3,$ and 4 respectively we obtain $X$'s, called Fermat numbers,

3, 5, 17, 257, and 65,537, which are prime. But the next Fermat number, $F_5 = 4,294,967,297$, is factorable into $641 \times 6,700,417$. For $n > 5$ the Fermat numbers rapidly become huge. A few are known to be composite. It is not known whether any higher ones are prime.

The seventeenth-century amateur mathematician Mersenne, an old friend of Fermat, studied numbers of the form $2^k - 1$, about which not very much is known. A Mersenne number $M = 2^k - 1$ may or may not be prime. For $k = 2, 3, 5, 7$ we get $M = 3, 7, 31, 127$, all primes. But if $k = 4$, $M = 15$, composite; $M$ must always be composite if $k$ is an even number greater than 2, for then

$$M = 2^{2j} - 1 = (2^j + 1)(2^j - 1)$$

In fact, $M$ is composite whenever $k$ is composite; but $M$ need not be prime if $k$ is prime. The first such composite $M$ is $M = 2^{11} - 1 = 23 \times 89$.

It had been conjectured that $2^k - 1$ would always be prime if $k$ were itself a Mersenne prime. We noted above that 3, 7, 31, 127 are the first four Mersenne primes, and it is true that $2^3 - 1$, $2^7 - 1$, $2^{31} - 1$, and $2^{127} - 1$ are all primes. $2^{11} - 1$ is not a prime, but the next, $2^{13} - 1 = 8191$, is prime. If the conjecture were correct then $2^{8191} - 1$ ought to be prime. This is such a large number that it was only recently tested on a computer; but it was found to be composite.

Returning now to Fermat numbers, it has been known since 1954 that all $F_n$ beyond $F_4$ are composite, up to and including $F_{12}$. A scattering of higher ones are also known to be composite, and one would like to know whether any $F_n$ is prime for $n > 4$. There was for a while a slight suspicion that $F_{13} = 2^{8192} + 1$ might be out of the usual run of things (that is, prime) because $2^{8191} - 1$, its Mersenne counterpart, showed a departure from the expected pattern. This conjecture, which never had more than the status of a wild guess, was proven incorrect in 1960 when "G. A. Paxson of the California Research Corporation, Richmond, Calif., showed that $F_{13}$ is composite, by a 6 hour calculation on an IBM 7090 computer." Thus one more Fermat number was brought into the fold of known composite ones, and the idea that there might be any significant alliance between the Fermat and the Mersenne numbers is probably wholly illusory.

Another conjecture about Mersenne numbers was that if $M_k = 2^k - 1$ is prime, then $M_k + 100$ is also prime. This happens to be so for all prime $M_k$ such that $k \leqslant 19$. But if $k > 19$, many composite counterexamples are known, and no further prime examples are known, giving rise to the new conjecture that if $M_k$ is prime, then perhaps $M_k + 100$ is *never* prime for $k > 19$.

The difficulty of course in working with Mersenne numbers and their much larger cousins, the Fermat numbers, is the staggering size which they soon attain. Even $F_{10}$ has 309 digits, and of $F_{36}$ Edouard Lucas remarked, "la bande de papier qui le contiendrait ferait le tour de la Terre." W. W. Rouse Ball states that the digits in $F_{73}$ "are so numerous that, if the number were printed in full with the type and number of pages used in this [his] book, many more volumes would be required than are contained in all the public libraries of the world." It is somewhat awesome that the unbelievably huge number $F_{1945}$ is now known to have a factor, namely $5 \times 2^{1947} + 1$. This is the world's record as of 1961.

We digress for a moment to give a hint as to how anything at all can be accomplished in this seemingly nightmare realm. The statement "12 is congruent to 5 modulo 7" is written $12 \equiv 5 \bmod 7$ and means that 12 and 5 have the same remainder when divided by 7. Thus $31 \equiv 1 \bmod 3$ and also $31 \equiv 10 \bmod 3$. Congruences behave like equations under many operations. One can easily prove that it is possible to multiply both sides of a congruence by the same integer, or to square both sides, without destroying the congruence. Thus: $4 \equiv 1 \bmod 3$. Multiplying by five: $20 \equiv 5 \bmod 3$; or squaring: $16 \equiv 1 \bmod 3$. The power of congruence arithmetic is illustrated by two examples.

(1) Every odd perfect square is congruent to 1 modulo 8. For every odd number is by

definition congruent to some one of 1, 3, 5, or 7 mod 8. Squaring both sides we have that every odd square is congruent to 1, 9, 25, or 49 mod 8; but each of these is congruent to 1 mod 8, which proves the statement.

(2) What is the remainder when $3^{100}$ is divided by 7?

Solution:
$$3^3 = 27 \equiv -1 \bmod 7$$
$$(3^3)^{33} = 3^{99} \equiv (-1)^{33} = -1 \bmod 7$$
$$3(3^{99}) = 3^{100} \equiv 3(-1) = -3 \equiv 4 \bmod 7$$

It may not be very valuable to know that when $3^{100}$ is divided by 7 the remainder is 4; but inasmuch as $3^{100}$ is a forty-eight digit number, we have obtained this information remarkably cheaply. It is only with the aid of such methods as these that one can hope to attain any results with numbers as large as the Fermat monsters.

Between 1880 and 1925, factors were obtained at great labor by various investigators for ten different Fermat numbers between $F_5$ and $F_{73}$. There the matter stood for twenty-eight years until John L. Selfridge knocked off two more on the SWAC, a modern electronic calculator. Then in 1956 and 1957 Selfridge and Raphael M. Robinson, on the same machine and with a fraction of the labor previously required, found factors for twenty more Fermat numbers, most of them larger by far than any that had been tackled before.

Although factors are known for several of the colossal $F_n$, it is interesting that two of the relatively smaller ones, $F_7$ and $F_8$, have defied the search for their factors, even though they have been known for fifty years to be composite. But even $F_7$ is a number of thirty-nine digits; and the factors themselves, whatever they are, have at least ten digits. Neither $F_7$ nor $F_8$ has any factor smaller than $2^{32} = 4{,}294{,}967{,}296$.

□

The question has sometimes been raised, how many primes are there of the form $(10^n - 1)/9$? It is easily seen that these numbers consist entirely of a string of ones. To date the only known values of $n$ which give primes are 1, 2, 19 and 23, yielding 1, 11, and the numbers consisting of nineteen and twenty-three 1's respectively. There may be no other $n$'s which give primes, or there may be an infinite number: nothing more is known except a partial list of the composite cases.

□

An easy formula which turns out a few primes is

$$X = n^2 - n + 41$$

It happens that for any $n$ less than 41, $X$ is a prime; but $n = 41$ yields $X = 41^2$, obviously composite. In the same way, and for the same reason, no polynomial function of $n$ with a constant term greater than 1 can ever yield primes beyond a certain point. One might suppose that the above formula works as well as it does because 41 is itself a prime. Then one would need only to find another prime $p > 41$ by use of this formula, and set it into a new formula

$$X = n^2 - n + p$$

to produce more new primes. Inasmuch as the procedure is constructive, it would serve to generate an unceasing supply of primes—but it doesn't work. The initial supposition is false. Seven is a prime, but

$$X = n^2 - n + 7$$

is not a prime-producing formula for all $n < 7$. In fact, if $n = 2$, $X = 9$. There are many such counterexamples. There seems to be no good reason why the expression happens to produce primes up to $n = p$ when $p = 41$.

☐

The *binomial coefficients* are the numerical parts of the elements in the expanded expression for $(a + b)^n$. If we multiply out $(a + b)^2 = (a + b)(a + b)$ we get $a^2 + 2ab + b^2$. Multiplying in turn by another $(a + b)$ yields $(a + b)^3 = a^3 + 3a^2b + 3ab^2 + b^3$. Now notice the law of formation of the coefficients. If we write down the skeleton of $(a^3 + 3a^2b + 3ab^2 + b^3)(a + b)$, it looks like this:

```
1   3   3   1
1   1
─────────────
1   3   3   1
    1   3   3   1
─────────────────
1   4   6   4   1
```

From each line we can easily write the next:

```
1   4   6   4   1
    1   4   6   4   1
─────────────────────
1   5  10  10   5   1
```

This semi-intuitive argument allows us to write down as many lines as we require of the Pascal Triangle of coefficients. The $n$th row gives the coefficients of $(a + b)^n$ (Figure 24);

[24]

```
            1       1

        1       2       1

    1       3       3       1

  1     4       6       4       1

 1    5     10      10      5       1

1    6    15     20      15     6      1

1   7   21     35     35     21    7     1

1  8   28    56     70    56    28    8    1

1  9  36   84   126   126   84   36   9   1
```

.   .   .   .   .   .   .   .   .   .   .   .

to obtain any number, simply add the two diagonally above it.

In the study of prime numbers, one comes upon a curious fact, readily proved: $n$ divides all the numbers (except the first and last) of the $n$th row if and only if $n$ is a prime. Thus 5 and 7 divide each number in their respective rows, but 8 and 9 do not. We have here a theoretically perfect test of primality—but it is useless from a practical point of view, because the labor of testing the binomial coefficients of a large number would be far greater than finding out whether it was prime by some more primitive method.

This theorem disposes of prime $n$'s; but what of composite ones? On the lines corresponding to composite $n$, *some* of the coefficients are evenly divisible by $n$ and some are not. Which ones? The answer to this interesting question is not known.

□

How many primes are there less than a given number? No one knows, although a formula for the exact number would be most welcome. What has been known since 1896 is that the number of primes less than $N$ approaches approximately $N/\log N$ as $N$ becomes very large.* This means that for large $N$ the probability

---

* The symbol "log" in this book, with no base indicated, means the *natural log*, or logarithm to the base $e$.

that any randomly selected integer "in the vicinity of $N$" should be prime approaches $1/\log N$, a quantity known as the *asymptotic density*.

In 1742 a man named Goldbach asked Leonard Euler whether he could prove or disprove the following conjecture: every even number greater than 2 can be written as the sum of two primes in at least one way. For example, $8 = 5 + 3$. (Sometimes it can be done in several ways: $48 = 7 + 41 = 11 + 37 = 17 + 31 = 19 + 29$.) Euler was unable to prove that this is true of all even numbers, nor was he able to find a counterexample. Goldbach's conjecture remains unsettled.

The so-called twin primes are pairs of primes whose difference is 2, like (11, 13) and (29, 31). They seem to be scattered throughout the number system. The statement that there are infinitely many of them is believed to be correct; but that is the most that we can say.

Essentially the only way to construct a table of primes up to $N$ is by a procedure known as the "sieve of Eratosthenes." Write down all the integers up to and including $N$. Strike out all multiples of 2 (except 2 itself), then all multiples of 3 (except 3) which are not already gone, then all remaining multiples of 5, and so on. The reason 5 is chosen after 3 is *not* that it is the next prime (we are not supposed to know that at this stage), but that it is the next number left: 4 is already gone. In this way all the composite numbers fall through the sieve, leaving only a list of the primes $\leqslant N$.

In 1956 S. M. Ulam and others made a table of what they christened *lucky numbers* by applying a slightly different sieve. Figure 25 shows the lucky numbers less than 100. (The slant lines indicate at what stage in the construction a number was eliminated.)

"In the sequence of all integers we strike out every second one, that is to say, all the even numbers. The first number remaining (apart from 1, which will not be counted) is 3. We shall now strike out every *third* integer, counting only the remaining ones, that is to say, this time we will strike out the integers 5, 11, 17, etc. In the remaining sequence the first number not used before is 7. Therefore we shall strike out every seventh number, counting among the remaining ones again. This will eliminate 19, etc. We proceed in this manner *ad infinitum.*" The numbers that remain, 1, 3, 7, 9, 13, ... are called the lucky numbers.

"It turns out that many asymptotic properties of the prime number sequence are shared by the lucky numbers. Thus, for example, their asymptotic density is $1/\log N$. The numbers of twin primes and of twin luckies exhibit remarkable similarity up to the integer

[25]

| 1 | 3 | ~~5~~ | 7 | 9 | ~~11~~ | 13 | 15 | ~~17~~ | ~~19~~ |
|---|---|---|---|---|---|---|---|---|---|
| 21 | ~~23~~ | 25 | ~~27~~ | ~~29~~ | 31 | 33 | ~~35~~ | 37 | ~~39~~ |
| ~~41~~ | 43 | ~~45~~ | ~~47~~ | 49 | 51 | ~~53~~ | ~~55~~ | ~~57~~ | ~~59~~ |
| ~~61~~ | 63 | ~~65~~ | 67 | 69 | ~~71~~ | 73 | 75 | ~~77~~ | 79 |
| ~~81~~ | 83 | ~~85~~ | 87 | ~~89~~ | ~~91~~ | 93 | ~~95~~ | ~~97~~ | 99 |

$n = 100,000$, the range which we have investigated on the machine. . . . It also happens that within the range investigated every even number is the sum of two lucky numbers."

These considerations present the primes in a new light. That so many properties hitherto thought to be sacred to the primes are shared by the luckies removes some of the charm and at the same time perhaps some of the significance of the primes. If these properties are consequences only of the fact that the primes are generated by a sieving process, and are not due to their primality, then many investigators have certainly been looking in the wrong direction. It can never be said that primes play no special role in the number system: a vast body of interesting and important theory of all kinds rests on primality. Nevertheless one somewhat reduces the preeminence of a mountain peak by discovering others of the same height.

Ulam has also considered the sequence 1, 2, 3, 4, 6, 8, 11, 13, 16, 18, 26, . . . formed according to the following rule: strike out from the sequence of natural numbers all (after 1 and 2) except those that can be obtained in one and only one way by adding two different earlier numbers of the set. Thus a number may be disqualified either because it can be obtained in too many ways, like 5; or because it cannot be obtained at all, like 23. The question is, what is the asymptotic density of this sequence?

There are certain pairs of primes, such as (13, 31) and (1229, 9221), where each is the "reversal" of the other. Perhaps the palindromic primes like 151 should also be counted, being their own reversals. Are there infinitely many such pairs? If so, what is their asymptotic density?

□

Suppose we want to determine the decimal expression for ⅟₁₃ by dividing 13 into 1. In the hope that you are agile at mental arithmetic, and to save space, we will use short division. If you prefer to do it by long division, the identical discussion applies. The exact form of a short division varies with the individual arithmetician; one way looks like this:

$$13\overline{)1.\ ^{1}0\ ^{10}0\ ^{9}0\ ^{12}0\ ^{3}0\ ^{4}0\ ^{1}0\ ^{10}0\ ^{9}0\ \ldots}$$
$$.\ 0\ 7\ 6\ 9\ 2\ 3,\ 0\ 7\ 6\ \ldots$$

Thus ⅟₁₃ has a *periodic* decimal expansion, of period 6 units long. The reason the expansion became periodic was that in the sequence of remainders 1, 10, 9, 12, 3, 4, 1, 10, etc., we happened to come around to a 1 again after six steps. Such a repetition need not have occurred at the seventh step, but it *must certainly* have occurred by at most the thirteenth step. because there are only twelve different remainders less than 13. Thus by the nature of the division process, every common fraction $1/n$

has a repeating decimal of period length at most $n - 1$. Once we arrive at a remainder we used before, the whole process repeats from there.

If we call $n - 1$ the maximal period, the question naturally arises, what, if any, integers $n$ have reciprocals $1/n$ whose decimal periods are maximal? The first is 7:

$$7)1.\ {}^10\ {}^30\ {}^20\ {}^60\ {}^40\ {}^50\ {}^10\ \dots$$
$$.\ 1\ \ 4\ \ 2\ \ 8\ \ 5\ \ 7,\ 1\ \dots$$

Note that each of the possible remainders, 1 through 6, appears before a repetition occurs.

There is no easy way known at present of predicting which $1/n$ have maximal periods. The next happens to be 17. A necessary condition is that $n$ be a prime, but this is not sufficient, as we noted when $n = 13$. The maximal $n$'s are scattered in apparently random fashion among the primes. One might expect that they would "thin out" with increasing $n$—that is, that they would become relatively scarcer, even among the primes; present information is insufficient to decide whether this is the case. About one-third of the first few primes have the maximal property, a proportion which remains approximately constant among the primes up to 1000. I do not know whether it has been checked for larger primes; but if it should turn out that the ratio of maximal $n$'s in any interval to the number of prime $n$'s in that same interval does indeed approach a non-zero constant as $N$ increases, then we have a class of numbers whose asymptotic density is not equal to but proportional to $1/\log N$.

□

We mention another unsolved problem about primes: Is there always at least one prime between every pair of consecutive squares? That is, is there always a prime between, for instance, 100 and 121, and between 625 and 676, etc.? The asymptotic density of the perfect squares is $1/(2\sqrt{N})$, which becomes rapidly smaller than $1/\log N$. The *probability* that two squares bridge a gap in the prime sequence tends to zero as $N$ increases; but that is not what is asked for. As usual, to answer a specific question about the primes is far more difficult than to answer a probabilistic or distributional question about them. And all attempts to link the primes to algebraic entities like perfect squares have so far met with complete failure.

□

The symbol $n!$ means the product of all integers up to and including $n$. Thus $4! = 1 \times 2 \times 3 \times 4 = 24$. It happens that $n! + 1$ is a perfect square when $n = 4$, 5, or 7. These are believed to be the only values of $n$ with this property; but a tentative proof offered in 1950 was subsequently shown to contain an invalidating oversight. It seems almost as difficult to connect the squares with the factorials as it is to connect them with the primes.

☐

Some numbers, like $13 = 9 + 4$ and $17 = 16 + 1$ can be expressed as the sum of two squares. But others, like 7, require four squares: $7 = 4 + 1 + 1 + 1$, and there is no sum with fewer squares because none are available except 1 and 4. Fermat proved that it is possible to express every positive integer, however large, as a sum of four or fewer squares; no integer requires five or more.

Is there a similar greatest number necessary and sufficient for decomposition of cubes, fourth powers, etc.? This is known as Waring's problem, after its originator. Within recent years it has been proven that every number can be expressed as the sum of nine or fewer cubes. $23 = 8 + 8 + 1 + 1 + 1 + 1 + 1 + 1 + 1$ is a number that actually requires nine.

If negative integers are admissible, the situation is quite different. Mordell says that it is easy to prove that every number can be expressed as the sum of at most five integer cubes, positive or negative; and that there is an unproved conjecture that four cubes suffice. For example, 23 now becomes expressible as $8 + 8 + 8 - 1$.

Nineteen fourth powers are required to make up 79, and it is conjectured that 19 is the answer to Waring's problem for fourth powers. The problem so far has been one of great difficulty, but the results of Hardy and Littlewood point in the direction of 19. For higher powers, less is known.

□

Euclid defined a perfect number as one which is equal to the sum of all its different divisors, like $1 + 2 + 3 = 6$. The number itself is of course not counted as one of the divisors, or no number could be perfect. Eight was called deficient, because $1 + 2 + 4 < 8$, whereas a number like 12 was said to be abundant: $1 + 2 + 3 + 4 + 6 > 12$. When number theory was still entangled in the meshes of numerology and mythology, the notion of the perfection or imperfection of a number had a more real significance than merely that of a name. The attachment of intrinsic qualities like goodness, malice, and godliness to numbers persists through human history, reaching down closer to the present day than perhaps we would willingly admit. Is it not true that 7 still carries a special aura because of the Sabbath day, and that for many people 13 wears a sinister cloak?

The only perfect numbers known to date are of the form $2^{k-1}(2^k - 1)$, where $2^k - 1$ is a *prime* Mersenne number. We have noted earlier that we lack a test for the primality of Mersenne numbers, which themselves are very large, so that the difficulty of finding perfect numbers is compounded. We do know that every even perfect number is of the above form; but whether odd perfect numbers exist is not known, nor whether there is an infinite or only a finite supply of perfect numbers. These questions no longer seem to be of very great importance to mathematics except as historical curios.

Leo Moser, of the University of Alberta, has proved (1949) that every number greater than 83,160 can be expressed as the sum of two abundant numbers. Some lesser numbers cannot be so expressed. Inasmuch as 12 is the smallest abundant number, certainly no number less than 24 can be so expressed. What is the largest integer not so expressible? The problem is completely solved for even numbers: 26, 28, 34, and 46 are the only even numbers greater than 24 which are not the sum of two abundant numbers. The situation among the odds is very different. Inasmuch as 945 is the smallest odd abundant number, we have the result that *all* odd numbers less than 957 are not expressible in the desired way. Thus the greatest odd number not so expressible lies between 957 and 83,160, and one need only devise a suitable sieve or other procedure to ferret it out. Compared with the amount of searching among enormous numbers required by many number-theoretic questions, this is a most modest demand. I do not know whether any work has been done toward a solution.

□

Ever since its publication in 1920, the standard reference work in number theory has been Eugene L. Dickson's great three-volume *History of the Theory of Numbers*. It is a catalog of all published contributions to this large branch of mathematical knowledge. "If it isn't in Dickson, it isn't in number theory." In Chapter 22 of Vol. 2, Dickson discusses the problem of finding an integer decomposable into the sum of two fourth powers in two different ways. The number 17, for example, is so decomposable in only one way:

$$17 = 1^4 + 2^4$$

Several solutions to the problem are known, and Dickson remarks that

$$635318657 = 158^4 + 59^4 = 133^4 + 134^4$$

is said to be the smallest. This is an unproved conjecture. I was therefore not a little surprised when one of my students announced that he had found a much smaller one, with not only two but three such decompositions! It developed that he was indulging in some mathematical high jinks at my expense, and had extended the problem to include decomposition into *Gaussian* integers, numbers of the form $a + bi$, where $a$ and $b$ are ordinary integers and $i = \sqrt{-1}$. Then

$$82 = 1^4 + 3^4 = (2i - 5)^4 + (2i + 5)^4$$

He further proved that 82 is the smallest natural number decomposable into two essentially different sums of fourth powers. (The other obvious decompositions of 17 such as $i^4 + 2^4$, $i^4 + (2i)^4$, are not essentially different from $1^4 + 2^4$.)

□

The field of Diophantine equations, those equations requiring solutions in whole numbers only, contains a host of difficult problems which continue to tantalize the number people. It happens that $3^2 + 4^2 = 5^2$ and that $3^3 + 4^3 + 5^3 = 6^3$. But this is "just luck." It is not true that $3^4 + 4^4 + 5^4 + 6^4 = 7^4$. This gives rise to the question of whether there are *any* other integers $a$, $k$, and $m$ satisfying

$$a^m + (a + 1)^m + \cdots + (a + k)^m$$
$$= (a + k + 1)^m$$

The problem has been extended farther. The system of equations:

$$a^3 + b^3 + c^3 + d^3 = x + y + z$$
$$a^6 + b^6 + c^6 + d^6 = x^2 + y^2 + z^2$$
$$a^3 + b^3 + c^3 = d^3$$

has solutions $a = 3$, $b = 4$, $c = 5$, $d = 6$,

$x = 91$, $y = 152$, $z = 189$. Find the general solution in integers, or prove that this is the only one.

Another question "hard to get a grip on" is, does the equation

$$m(m + 1)(m + 2) = n(n + 1)(2n + 1)$$

have any solutions in positive integers besides the trivial one $m = n = 1$?

□

Some typical unsolved Diophantine problems follow.

(1) Is there an infinite number of primes of the form $n^2 + 1$? The first few are given by $n = 1, 2, 4, 6, 10, 14, 16, 20$. The same question can be asked for numbers of the form $n! + 1$. Note that neither of these questions is the same as the one asked earlier about $n! + 1$. A much harder (non-Diophantine) problem would be, if the answer to either of the above questions is "yes," then what is the asymptotic density of (a) the set of numbers of the prescribed form, and (b) the set of generating $n$'s?

(2) Are there three integers whose product equals the cube of their sum? In other words, does the Diophantine equation

$$(x + y + z)^3 = xyz$$

have a solution? Don't forget that negative integers are admissible. This looks like an absurdly easy problem; yet it has been unsuccessfully begging to be answered for some time.

(3) It is known that the number of integral solutions of

$$x^3 - y^2 = 7$$

is finite, but we do not know all the solutions, nor even how many there are.

(4) Are there any two consecutive numbers of the form $a^b$, both $a$ and $b$ positive integers, except $2^3$ and $3^2$? It is not even known whether or not *three* consecutive numbers of this form exist.

(5) Is there an infinite number of triples of *consecutive* primes in arithmetic progression, like 3, 5, 7 and 47, 53, 59?

(6) For what $m$ does the equation

$$x^3 + y^3 + z^3 + w^3 = m$$

have (positive or negative) integer solutions in $x, y, z, w$? This is another form of the conjecture mentioned on page 91. What is wanted is a test, valid for all $m$.

(7) Even when it is known that a certain $m$ gives a solution of (6), it is not known whether there exists an infinite number of other solutions for that $m$.

(8) The conjecture of (6) can be strengthened by asking whether there is always a solution even when we require that $w = z$. That is, does

$$x^3 + y^3 + 2z^3 = m$$

have a solution for every $m$? The least value of $m$ for which no solution is known, nor even whether a solution exists, is 76.

(9) The sharper requirement

$$x^3 + y^3 + z^3 = m$$

is known to have solutions for certain special but by no means all $m$. For example, it is not known whether a solution exists if $m = 30$.

(10) What are the conditions on general $a$, $b$, for solvability in integers of the equation $x^2 + y^2 + z^2 - axyz = b$?

(11) Does the Diophanatine equation $ax + by = c$, with $a$ and $b$ relatively prime (no common factor except 1), have an infinite number of solutions such that $x$ and $y$ are both primes?

(12) If the answer to (11) is yes, is it true in the special case $a = 1$, $b = -1$, $c = 2$? This is of course Goldbach's conjecture.

(13) The equation $x^4 + y^4 + 64 = z^4$ has the solution-triples $(x, y, z)$: $(1, 2, 3)$; $(7, 8, 9)$; $(21, 36, 37)$. Are there any others? An infinite number? Are there any with $z - y \neq 1$?

(14) Conjecture: If $p$ is a prime congruent to 3 modulo 4 (meaning it has remainder 3 when divided by 4), and if $U$ is the value of $x$ in the least primitive solution of the Diophantine equation $y^2 = px^2 + 1$, then $U$ is never evenly divisible by $p$. Examples:

$$4 = 3 \times 1^2 + 1$$
$$64 = 7 \times 3^2 + 1$$

The conjecture has been verified for all $p < 18,000$, but never proved.

The list could go on almost indefinitely. If

you are interested in Diophantine analysis, the field, like most difficult ones, is wide open.

□

Let $f(x, y)$ be a general cubic equation in $x$ and $y$ with rational coefficients. No general method is known for finding a solution of this equation in rational numbers—that is, a point on the curve, both of whose co-ordinates are rational.

H. Davenport has proven that a homogeneous cubic equation in $n$ variables $f(x_1, x_2, \cdots x_n) = 0$ always has solutions in integers (not all zero) provided $n \geqslant 29$; but this is probably not best possible. Davenport guesses that 10 might be.

□

Does there exist a rectangular parallelepiped (box) all of whose edges and face diagonals are of integral length, and the length of whose main diagonal is also an integer? This is a Diophantine problem, a sort of extended Pythagorean theorem.

□

Single, isolated number questions are often difficult to attack because they fail to fall into any known pattern or category. Possibly for this reason also they possess less charm than some of the bigger problems. One such nu-

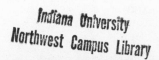

merical question is to determine whether or not $2^7 = 128$ is the only power of 2 of two or more digits each of which is a power of 2 (recalling that $1 = 2^0$). Professor R. J. Walker, who proposed the problem, supplies a hint for those interested in attacking it. It is not possible to find a positive integer, $r$, large enough so that no power of 2 could have its last $r$ digits all powers of 2. The opposite is true. In fact, for any integer $r$ there exist powers of 2 such that all of the last $r$ digits are either 1 or 2.

Starting with $a_0 = 1$ and $a_1 = 1$, let the law of formation of subsequent members of a sequence be $a_{n+1} = a_n + a_{n-1}$. This law generates the famous Fibonacci Sequence:

1, 1, 2, 3, 5, 8, 13, 21, 34, 55, 89, 144, 233, . . .

Many interesting relations come out of a study of the Fibonacci numbers.

It is thought that 144 is the only square Fibonacci number besides 1, but to the best of my knowledge this has never been proved.

The third, fifth, seventh, and thirteenth numbers of the sequence are primes. We are thus tempted to guess that, if $F_n$ stands for the $n$th Fibonacci number, $F_n$ is prime whenever $n$ is prime. But this pretty conjecture fails at an early stage: $F_{19}$ is composite. Not only is there no known device predicting which $F_n$ are prime, but it is not even known whether the number of prime Fibonacci numbers is finite. If it is infinite, what is their asymptotic density?

# 6

# Topological problems

Numbers are old friends: we grew up with them and we see them every day. They have become part of our life. Although numbers are really very abstract entities, we nevertheless find them easy to understand through long familiarity and training.

The field of topology is quite another story. We cope with it every day too, but without thinking and without systematizing our language and our techniques as we have done with numbers. We know that a left glove will not fit a right hand; yet why does a telephone receiver, shaped to curve between mouth and ear, fit either side of the face? Why do some configurations of a piece of string constitute knots whereas others are mere loops that disappear when the string is pulled? How are the

[26]

three rings in the trade mark of a well-known brewery linked together, or are they linked at all? (See Figure 26: no one ring passes through any other ring; yet they cannot be pulled apart.) That every direction is south to a person standing at the north pole is the fault of our latitude-longitude system. Inasmuch as the polar regions are becoming more important places than they once were, it might be convenient to adopt a co-ordinate grid on which there would be no such difficulty anywhere on earth. Is such a grid possible?

These are topological questions. Their formulation and consideration by mathematical methods was not even attempted until recent times. Topology is a twentieth-century product; hence one might expect that it abounds with unsolved problems, and it does. But although some of them are easily stated, for

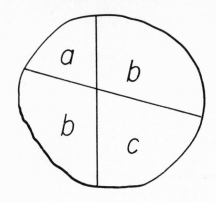

most of them we require first a language in which to frame the question. This language, unlike that of the number system, is not familiar to most of us.

The oldest and best-known unsolved problem in topology is also the easiest to explain. It is the famous four-color problem. In making a map, one wishes to use different colors for any two countries with all or part of a border in common. If two countries come together at only one point, like *a* and *c* in Figure 27, they are not considered to have a common border; for they could be colored alike without confusion. Some maps require four colors, as in Figure 28. If this map represents an island, the ocean can either be disregarded or colored the same as *b*: in either case no more than

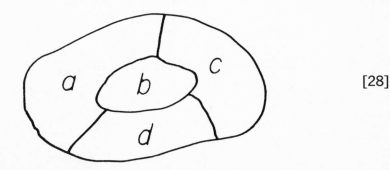

four colors are required, but three will not do.

The question is, are there any maps which require five colors? None are known, but on the other hand no proof exists that four colors are always sufficient. (It is known that *five* colors are always sufficient.) The problem has been driven out to this stage: it has been shown that no map of fewer than thirty-five regions can require more than four colors. Thus if any five-color maps exist, they are very complicated ones.

Martin Gardner, whose monthly column in *Scientific American* since 1957 has contained many amusing problems, made an error in a piece of humorous science fiction which he wrote in 1952 entitled "The Island of Five Colors." In it he implied that the four-color theorem states that no five regions can all have boundaries common to the other four. This is true, but it is easy to prove and is *not* equivalent to the four-color theorem. The story was reprinted in 1958 in Clifton Fadiman's "Fantasia Mathematica." Mr. Gardner ruefully acknowledges the slip in the September 1960 *Scientific American,* where he states (p. 218) that he is still receiving proofs of his version of the theorem from excited readers who think that they have solved the classical problem.

The coloring problem is the same on the surface of a sphere as it is on a plane, but on the surface of a torus (doughnut) it is quite different. If the earth were a torus it might be necessary to use seven colors to map its surface, but surely no more than seven. Oddly enough, this seemingly more difficult theorem has been proved.

☐

Two sets, *A* and *B*, are said to be topologically equivalent if there is a one-to-one correspondence between all the members of *A* and all the members of *B* that is continuous both ways.

One-to-one means just what it says: to every member of *A* can be matched one member of *B*, no more and no less, and vice versa. Note that we do not have to *count* the members of either set to be able to decide whether such a correspondence exists. The phrase means only that such a correspondence *can be* observed. Thus if *A* is the set of points on a line segment 1 inch long and *B* is the set of points on a line segment 2 inches long, then *A* and *B* are topologically equivalent. One need only demonstrate that they can be matched one-to-one, as shown in Figure 29. In precisely the same way, a semicircular arc 1 inch long with the end points of the semicircle deleted is equivalent to a straight line of

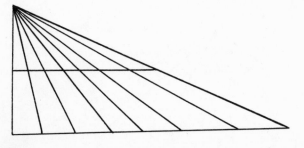

[29]

infinite length. In Figure 30, each radial line matches one point of the arc with one point of the line. The "continuity both ways" requires, loosely speaking, that points *close to* point $P$ of one set are matched with points close to point $P'$, the image or map of $P$, in the second set. The definition of continuity can be made precise, but this one will do for our purposes.

A one-to-one correspondence of the type described above is called a homeomorphism, and two sets are topologically equivalent if they are homeomorphic.

One might suppose that a homeomorphism is equivalent to a deformation transformation, but that is only one kind of homeomorphism. Two sets have been described as topologically equivalent if one can be transformed into the other by "kneading and stretching without breaking and tearing." This is true, but it is not the whole truth. The set of all points on two spherical surfaces (of different radii) tangent internally is topologically equivalent to the set of all points on the same two surfaces tangent externally: the necessary homeomorphism exists. But it is not possible to transform the first set into the second by a pure deformation.

[30]

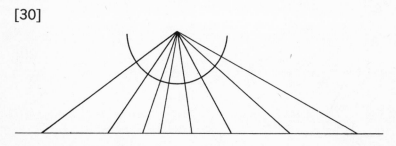

Consider now a circular disk: the set of all points on and inside a circle in the plane. An interesting theorem of L. E. J. Brouwer states that any homeomorphism of such a disk onto itself leaves at least one point fixed. Two questions connected with this transformation are raised by Ulam. If a homeomorphism maps the points $p$ of a disk onto the points $p'$ of the disk, then do there exist arbitrarily small triangles $p_1p_2p_3$ congruent to the triangles formed by connecting the image points $p'_1p'_2p'_3$? One might think that such triples of points could be found in the neighborhood of the fixed point. On the other hand, some such triples may occur in an entirely different part of the disk. Note that the question does not demand that any one of $p_1$, $p_2$, $p_3$ remain fixed, nor does it say that a whole triangle must be lifted bodily by the homeomorphism and set down in a new position. It asks only about some three distinct points. If the answer to the above question is yes, a second question is, do such triangles exist with prescribed angles?

By *the points on a circle* we mean the set of points on the circumference only, not inside the circle. It is clear that the set of points on a circle does not have Brouwer's fixed-point property. A perfectly satisfactory homeomorphism onto itself is a simple rotation of $n$ degrees, $n \neq 360$, which leaves no point fixed.

Connectivity is another property that means roughly what it says. The points interior to a circle are connected; so are the points on a line segment. The *complement* of a set is all the points of a space (such as the plane) *not* members of the set. Thus the complement of the set of points on a circle is a disconnected set: it consists of all the points outside the circle and all the points inside the circle and they are mutually disjoint, being separated by the circle itself.

We can now state the next problem. If $C$ is a bounded plane continuum whose complement is connected, does $C$ necessarily have the fixed-point property? Note that it is the connectivity of the *complement* that is important: a washer-shaped area is connected, but its complement is not, and a washer-shaped area certainly does not have the fixed-point property. It is thought, but it has never been proved, that the answer to the above question is yes.

An *arc* is a set topologically equivalent to a straight-line segment. We have already shown that a straight-line segment is topologically equivalent to a part of itself. Is there any plane continuum with more than one point which is topologically equivalent to each continuum in it with more than one point, which is *not* an arc? For many years the answer was thought to be no, but in 1948 E. E. Moise found an affirmative example. The problem as to whether or not there are still other examples remains unsolved.

□

Two curves in ordinary three-dimensional space are said to be mutually *enlaced* if there exists no homeomorphism of the whole space under which the images of the two curves are contained in disjoint geometric spheres. There is at present no workable analytical criterion by which one can decide whether two given curves are enlaced.

A topological property somewhat different from enlacement is *knottedness*. The characterization of knots is by no means complete. The following discussion goes beyond the knot itself to the 3-space surrounding it. "It would be interesting to describe the system of magnetic lines of force due to a current flowing on a knotted (infinitely thin) wire. In particular, suppose the current flows through a 'cloverleaf' knot. Does the system of lines of magnetic force in space surrounding the knot reflect topologically the knottedness of the curve? Such systems of curves may exhibit considerable topological complexity even when generated by currents flowing on straight lines, as shown by calculations on the properties of lines of force due to currents flowing on the three straight lines $x = 1, y = 0; y = 1, z = 0; z = 1, y = 1$."

# 7

# Probability
# and combinatorial problems

There is no branch of mathematics quite so deceptively tricky as probability theory. Doubtless more erroneous answers have appeared in print to questions in probability than in any other field. Even the experts have occasionally been deceived. Let these words serve as a warning to any novice too eager to plunge into a problem that asks, "What are the chances . . . ?"

To illustrate one of the pitfalls we cite a famous easy example. There are three cards, with no markings on them, alike except for their coloring. One is red on both sides, one is red on one side and white on the other, and the third is white on both sides. After shuffling them in a closed bag we draw one out and lay it on the table, no one having had any opportunity to see the side that is down. Suppose the side showing is red. Then obviously it is not the white-white card, and it must be one of the other two. If it is the red-red card the other side is red, and if it is the red-white card the other side is white. It seems as if one might bet even money on either possibility.

But that analysis is faulty. The chances that the under side is red are not even, but two to one in favor. The point, and it is the important point missed in many probability questions, is that the events in doubt must be *equally likely*. There are two possibilities, to be sure; but they are not equally likely. We may be looking at side No. 1 of the red-red card, or at side No. 2 of the red-red card, or at the red side of the red-white card. These three possibilities *are* equally likely. Two of them will lead to red on the concealed face, only one to white.

A more subtle difficulty in deciding what events are equally likely arises in the following problem. Suppose we ask someone to draw "at random" a chord in a given circle. What is the probability that this chord will be longer than the side of an equilateral triangle inscribed in the circle? There are at least two ways of defining the randomness of the chord. We can select a point $A$ on the circle and consider the chords with one end at $A$. Since the other end of any such chord is equally likely to lie on any other point of the circle, we can

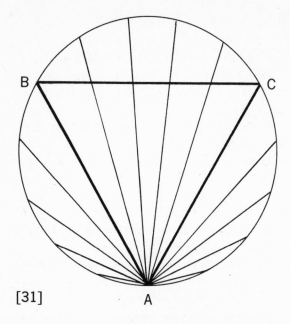

A

distribute points uniformly around the circle
to serve as these other ends. Now inscribe the
triangle with a vertex at *A* (Figure 31). It appears equally likely that the random chord
should intersect one of the three equal arcs
$\widehat{AB}$, $\widehat{BC}$, $\widehat{CA}$. Thus the probability that it
is longer than the line *AB* is ⅓. On the other
hand, if we distribute our sample of chords at
equally spaced intervals along a diameter
(Figure 32), we get the result that half of
them are now longer than *AB*, for a conflicting answer of ½ to the probability question.

Which result is correct? Quite possibly
neither. The notions of "random" and "equally
probable" are not satisfactorily defined in this
problem, so that although we may think we

know what a random chord is, in fact we do not.

Frank Hawthorne, New York State's supervisor of mathematics education, once posed this question: In a rectangle twice as long as it is wide, what is the probability that three random points are the vertices of an obtuse triangle? Here there seems to be less difficulty about randomicity. One can make the problem arithmetical by placing the rectangle on a co-ordinate system and randomizing the points numerically through their co-ordinates. Nevertheless it remains unsolved.

It is not surprising that the next problem has been on the unsolved docket for twenty years. Three men have respectively $l$, $m$, and $n$ coins which they match so that the odd man wins. Whenever all coins appear alike they re-

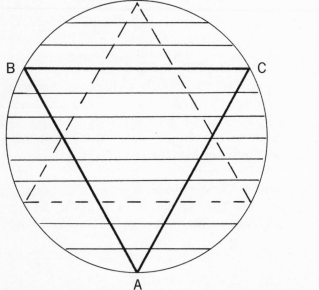

[32]

peat the throw. Find the average number of tosses required until one man is forced out of the game.

☐

The study of probability hinges on an analysis of the permutations and combinations involved. That some combinatorial problems are quite easy to state but very difficult to solve is evidenced by the postage stamp problem: in how many ways is it possible to fold a strip of $n$ postage stamps? The folds are to occur only along the perforations between stamps, and a strip means the kind that comes out of a coil machine, one stamp wide. Of course the answer for certain small values of $n$ can be found by actual experiment. What is wanted is a formula or an analysis for arbitrary $n$.

A generalization with an added dimension of difficulty is: given a road map of $N$ folds, in how many ways can it be re-folded? Faced with an over-stuffed glove compartment, you have probably already worked with this problem!

Here is an abstract combinatorial problem: The distinct pairs of $n$ objects, $n$ odd, are arranged in $n$ columns so that each column contains $\frac{n-1}{2}$ pairs and no one object occurs more than once in the same column, without regard to the order of the column or of the

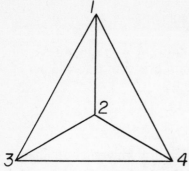

pairs in a column. Determine the number of different ways in which this can be done. To illustrate, if $n = 3$ and the objects are A, B, and C, then the only pairings are AB, AC, and BC, and since the columns are only one pair long, that is the total answer: one way. If $n = 5$, A, B, C, D, and E can be paired and placed in columns in several ways. Two of them are:

(1) $\begin{cases} AB & AC & AD & AE & CE \\ CD & DE & BE & BC & BD \end{cases}$

(2) $\begin{cases} AB & AC & CD & AE & CE \\ DE & BD & BE & BC & DA \end{cases}$

How many ways are there? More generally, how many ways when 5 is extended to $n$?

□

Herbert Phillips, who conducted a famous problem column under the pen name Caliban, once posed the following.

"*The five red balls.* The Professor had a number of balls of various colours. He put a certain number (the colours of which were not known) in a bag, and the class then drew out five at random. All five were red. 'That that would happen,' said the Professor, 'was exactly an even money chance.' How many balls in all had he put in the bag, and how many of them were red ones?"

Caliban's published solution was that the bag originally contained nine red balls and one not-red ball. Some further questions suggest themselves. (1) Is the Caliban solution the only one possible for five? (2) Can the problem be solved if "five" is replaced by "six" throughout? (3) Is there a general solution? Because the mathematics becomes technical, the interested reader is referred to the notes for a discussion of these questions.

☐

Each of $n$ points in the plane is joined to every other one by continuous curves. What is the least number of intersections of these curves?

If this least number is called $X_n$, we note from Figure 33 that four points can be mutually interconnected with no intersections, so that $X_4 = 0$. Figure 34 seems to indicate that

[34]

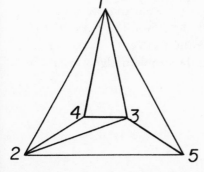

points 4 and 5 cannot be connected without an intersection with a previously drawn line. This has in fact been proven, so that $X_5 = 1$. It is probably true that $X_6 = 3$, but nothing further is known. What is wanted is a general formula for $X_n$ or a procedure for finding $X_n$. The same problem on the surface of a sphere is also essentially unsolved.

☐

We close this chapter with an amusing little question which can hardly be classed as a problem, but which points up the importance of precision in thought and meaning where averages, probabilities, and expectation are involved. If nothing is known about $x$ save that it lies between 9 and 11, what is the most likely value of $x$? If this is too hopelessly vague, the question may be better phrased as follows: if you are forced to guess the value of $x$, with a penalty for per cent error, what guess will make your maximum penalty the least? At first glance you might guess 10, which cannot be in error by more than 1 in either direction; but 9.9 would be a better guess. For 9.9 can be in error by no more than 10% of the true value, no matter what that is; whereas if the true value is close to 9, the guess of 10 is in error by more than 11%.

One can solve the problem algebraically by

selecting $x$ so that the maximum per cent error in both directions is the same:

$$\frac{x - 9}{9} = \frac{11 - x}{11}$$

Now observe what happens if we simply widen the range: suppose nothing is known about $x$ except that it lies between 1 and 100. The same process yields an $x$ very close to 2 (actually 1.98). And this is the right answer; the maximum error is now about 100% in either direction. But it raises doubts as to whether minimizing the maximum possible per cent error is always a suitable interpretation of obtaining a "most likely value." Few people would accept 2 as a best guess between 1 and 100. The fact is, of course, that there is no most likely value in the sense of probabilities. Lacking other data, every number is equally likely.

# 8

# Problems of infinite sets

A rational number, $p/q$, is a number expressible as the quotient of two integers, $p$ and $q$.
If the rationals are interpreted as points on the
real line, one can always find a new rational
point between any two given rationals, however close: their average, for instance. That is
to say, the rationals are *dense* on the real line.
In the same way, the points whose co-ordinates
are both rational are dense in the plane.

Ulam asks whether it is possible to characterize or describe the sets of points in the plane
such that the distance between any two of
their points is rational. He asks further whether
such a set can be dense in the plane. All the
rational points on a straight line comprise a
set which answers the first question in the

affirmative; but a one-dimensional set is not
what is wanted.

☐

In the Cantor theory, two infinite sets have
the same cardinal number if the members of
one set can be placed in one-to-one correspondence in some way with the members of
the other. Any set whose members can be
paired off against the set of positive integers is
given the cardinal number $\aleph_0$, read aleph-
null. Thus the set of perfect squares has car-
dinality $\aleph_0$. The matching may be done in
the obvious way:

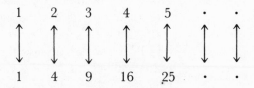

Every number $N$ is matched with an $N^2$ and
vice versa. We note that even though the set
of squares is itself a subset of (contained in)
the set of integers, it has the cardinal number
of the parent set. In the theory of the infinite,
the whole is frequently no greater than one of
its parts.

The set of all points, rational and irrational,
on the real line is known to have a cardinal
number greater than $\aleph_0$. By his now-famous
"diagonal procedure," Cantor showed that

this set of real points cannot be matched one-to-one with the integers. In fact its cardinal number is $2^{\aleph_0}$.

If a determinant of order $n$ is expanded into an algebraic polynomial the expansion contains $n$ ! terms. A determinant defined as the limit of a determinant of order $n$ as $n \to \infty$ can be a perfectly respectable member of the mathematical household, and it is known that its expansion contains $2^{\aleph_0}$ terms. What is not known is how to construct a one-to-one correspondence between these terms and the $2^{\aleph_0}$ points on the real line.

☐

The most famous unsolved problem associated with infinite sets is Cantor's *continuum hypothesis:* $2^{\aleph_0} = \aleph_1$. This means that the next larger transfinite number after $\aleph_0$ is the number of points on a line, the "power of the continuum." The problem of course is to prove or disprove the hypothesis. Cantor guessed that it was so. It is equivalent to the proposition that every infinite subset of the continuum has either the power of the set of integers or the power of the whole continuum; there is nothing in between.

In 1947 Kurt Gödel summarized the meager existing information on the subject in a paper in the *American Mathematical Monthly,* and noted further questions concerning it. Not even an upper bound can be assigned to the power of the continuum. "It is undecided whether it is regular or singular, accessible or inaccessible, and . . . what its character of confinality is." These terms are defined in the paper.

Gödel inclines to the belief that the conjecture will ultimately be disproved. He bases this on several considerations, among them the exceedingly unexpected and implausible consequences derivable from an acceptance of the hypothesis. Peculiar and "unbelievable" theorems are not, of course, to be taken as conclusive disproof of anything. Mathematics is full of perfectly valid results which seem intuitively impossible (such as the Banach-Tarski Theorem mentioned in Chapter 1). Nevertheless as evidence continues to pile up, one begins to wonder.

A new example of the weird and wonderful possibilities connected with the hypothesis is that the following conjecture implies $2^{\aleph_0} = \aleph_1$. The Euclidean plane is the union of three sets, $E_i (i = 1, 2, 3)$, such that, for some three straight lines in the plane $D_i (i = 1, 2, 3)$, the set $E_i$ intersects every straight line parallel to $D_i$ in only a finite number of points. In fact, a considerably weaker hypothesis of this sort also can be shown to imply the continuum hypothesis.

# 9

# Variational problems

Questions asking what shape, what path, or what form will yield a minimal or optimal result are known as variational problems. We have already met some in Chapters 1 and 2. A classical question known as Plateau's problem leads to a number of similar questions. J. A. F. Plateau asked for the surface of smallest area bounded by a given closed non-plane curve in space. The general Plateau problem was solved by Tibor Rado and by Jesse Douglas in 1930–31.

What is the shortest curve joining two points on an ellipse and at the same time dividing the area of the ellipse into two equal simply connected pieces? Is the problem solvable if the two points coincide? If a simple closed curve lies on the surface of a sphere, what is the surface of minimal area through this curve dividing the sphere into two equal volumes? Inasmuch as this is Plateau's problem with an added condition, it may not be solvable. In fact the answers to all these questions are unknown.

☐

Required: through a given point $P$ inside a triangle, to draw a line cutting off ⅓ of the area of the triangle. To describe how to do this with ruler and compass might be a very difficult assignment, perhaps impossible; but that is not the problem we wish to pose. If $P$ is the centroid of the triangle the construction is doomed to failure; no line through the centroid can cut off ⅓ of the area of the triangle. Yet through some other points $P$ such lines certainly exist. The problem is to determine the size and shape of the area such that if $P$ is in that area no line through $P$ cuts off ⅓ of the triangle. Another way to state the problem is this: imagine that all possible lines cutting off ⅓ of the area of the triangle have been drawn. There will remain some part of the triangle untouched by any lines. What part is this? At present it is not even known whether it is simply connected.

☐

In *What is Mathematics?*, Richard Courant and Herbert Robbins describe a mechanical method for "solving" various aspects of Plateau's problem. If a wire framework is dipped into soapsuds and carefully withdrawn, a film of soap will cling to the frame, stretched to form a minimal surface because of the surface tension of the film, in the same way that a soap bubble takes the form of a sphere because in that way it contains a given volume of air with the least surface. If a wire model of a cube is dipped into the suds, the result is a system of thirteen nearly plane surfaces that take the form indicated in Figure 35. But the surfaces are not all plane, nor is the small central one exactly square. Courant and Robbins call it "a challenging unsolved problem" to find or characterize these surfaces in some analytic fashion. As far as I know, no progress has been made on the problem in the twenty years since the book was published.

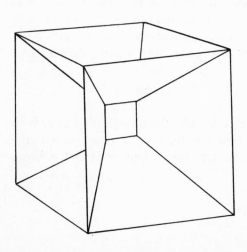

[35]

"Suppose two segments are given in the plane, each of length one. One is asked to move the first segment continuously, without changing its length, to make it coincide at the end of the motion with the second given interval in such a way that the sum of the lengths of the two paths described by the end points should be a minimum. What is the general rule for this minimum motion? . . . One could require alternately [he means alternatively] that instead of the sum, the square root of the sum of the squares of the lengths described by the end-points should be minimum.

"More generally, one could pose an analogous problem of the 'most economical' motion given a geometrical object $A$ and another $B$ congruent to it and requiring the motion from $A$ to $B$ to be such that a sum or integral of the lengths of paths described by individual points be minimum. . . . One motivation behind the consideration of such questions is that in certain problems of mechanics of continua, e.g. in hydrodynamics, the motions that are most prevalent are singled out by extremal principles not unlike the above; but of course operating in a space of infinitely many dimensions."

□

A piece of flexible chain suspended from both ends takes the form of a *catenary,* a curve whose equation is well known. If such a hanging chain is suspended over a liquid, say water, so that part of it hangs in the water, the curve will change into a new catenary under water and two pieces of another new catenary above the water. Is it possible to write an equation for the angle made by the chain as it enters the water, in terms of the other factors that affect the problem? This does not sound very difficult, but when the problem was proposed ten years ago there were no takers.

# 10

## Problems of analysis

The great branch of mathematics known as analysis has been the major working field of the past two centuries. It is the logical outgrowth of the calculus, and is also the material on which much so-called applied mathematics depends. It is safe to say that over half of the entire body of mathematics consists partially or wholly of analysis. We present here a few problems which have no connection with one another except that they are all more or less analytic. The first is a relatively simple question in algebra.

You will recall that a geometric progression is an expression of the form

$$a + ar + ar^2 + \cdots + ar^n$$

If the common ratio $r$ is numerically less than 1, the sum still has meaning when $n \to \infty$. If $a = \frac{1}{2}$ and $r = \frac{1}{2}$, we have the familiar series

$$\frac{1}{2} + \frac{1}{4} + \frac{1}{8} + \frac{1}{16} + \cdots + \frac{1}{2^n} + \cdots$$

whose sum is 1. This series has the property that there exists a term (for example the first) equal to the sum of all terms from that point on. The question is, does any other geometric series have this property? Incidentally, the given series is probably the only one for which *every* term will serve to illustrate the property, but that is not certain either.

☐

Paul Erdos has proposed (and solved) many nasty questions involving inequalities. Here are three unsolved ones, presented without further comment.

(1) If $m$ and $n$ are integers satisfying

$$\left(1 - \frac{1}{m}\right)^n > \frac{1}{2}, \qquad \left(1 - \frac{1}{m-1}\right)^n < \frac{1}{2}$$

prove the relations

$$(m-1)^n > (m-2)^n + (m-3)^n + \cdots + 1^n$$
$$(m+1)^n < m^n + (m-1)^n + \cdots + 1^n$$

Show also that the inequality

$$m^n > (m-1)^n + (m-2)^n + \cdots + 1^n$$

is true in infinitely many instances, but is also untrue in infinitely many instances.

(2) Let $a_1 < a_2 < \cdots < a_n \leqslant 2n$ be a sequence of positive integers. Then

$$\max\,(a_i, a_j) > \frac{38n}{147} - c$$

where $c$ is independent of $n$, and $(a_i, a_j)$ denotes the greatest common divisor of $a_i$ and $a_j$. We are asked to (a) prove the statement, (b) find $c$, and (c) show that this is a best possible estimate.

(3) Let $a_1 < a_2 < \cdots < a_k \leqslant n$; $b_1 < b_2 < \cdots < b_l \leqslant n$, be two sequences of integers such that all the products $a_i b_j$ are different. Prove that

$$kl < c(n^2/\log n)$$

Erdos says that if this is true, for some universal constant $c$, then it is a best possible estimate.

□

It is known that there exist infinitely many rational integral algebraic equations with integer coefficients, the leading one of which is unity, with all but one root occurring within a specified interval. If you wished to make use of this fact, it would doubtless be convenient to select one with small coefficients. Is there any procedure by which this can be done? In particular, what is the equation of degree $n$ fulfilling the above conditions and having in some sense the "smallest" coefficients?

☐

A scholar needs considerable training before he attacks new work in a field that has been the favorite of the masters. We suggest therefore, that if you do not have at least a passing acquaintance with the language and spirit of calculus, perhaps you would be well advised to pass over the remaining two problems.

A *function* is a connection between two variables. When you drew "graphs" of circles and parabolas in high school, you were sketching pictures of functions. Thus $y = x^2$ *connects* $y$ and $x$ through the squaring process: the equation says, whatever value $x$ has, square it to obtain the value of $y$. The *inverse* function is the one which makes the opposite statement in the algebraic sense: Whatever value $y$ has, square it to obtain the value of $x$, $x = y^2$. Note that we can solve this for $y$, obtaining $y = \pm \sqrt{x}$. If we agree to neglect the negative possibility, so as to talk only about single-valued functions, we have $y = \sqrt{x}$ as the inverse of the function $y = x^2$.

In the functional notation we say that $f^{-1}(x)$ is the inverse of $f(x)$. Observe that $f^{-1}(f(x)) = x$. This is indeed the *definition* of an inverse function. In the example, if $f(x) = x^2$, then $f^{-1}(x) = \sqrt{x}$ because

$$f^{-1}(f(x)) = \sqrt{x^2} = x$$

The inverse function is the one that "undoes" the work of the given function. Likewise $f(f^{-1}(x)) = x$, as exemplified by $(\sqrt{x})^2 = x$. Other examples of inverse functions are $x + 2$ and $x - 2$; $\log x$ and $e^x$.

Now we have to jump into second-year calculus and talk about expansions in power series. Suppose $f(x)$ has a power series representation

$$f(x) = a_0 + a_1 x + a_2 x^2 + \cdots$$

Let us seek

$$f^{-1}(x) = b_0 + b_1 x + b_2 x^2 + \cdots$$

such that $f(f^{-1}(x)) = x$. That is, we want the power series for the inverse function, if it exists. The problem then is to determine the $b$'s so that

$$x = a_0 + a_1[b_0 + b_1 x + b_2 x^2 + \cdots]$$
$$+ a_2[b_0 + b_1 x + b_2 x^2 + \cdots]^2 + \cdots$$

Without loss of generality one can arrange things so that $a_0 = b_0 = 0$ and $a_1 = b_1 = 1$. It is then possible to determine the rest of the $b_n$, one by one, in terms of the given $a_n$, by the method of equating coefficients of like powers of $x$; but the calculations become messy and

135

no pattern is apparent. "Satisfactory formulas expressing the $b_n$ in terms of the $a_n$ are not known [1956]."

□

The infinite series

$$1 + \frac{1}{2^2} + \frac{1}{3^2} + \frac{1}{4^2} + \cdots$$

might or might not converge (it turns out that it does). Likewise we might investigate

$$1 + \frac{1}{2^3} + \frac{1}{3^3} + \frac{1}{4^3} + \cdots$$

More generally, one writes $\zeta(n)$, read "zeta of $n$," where

$$\zeta(n) = 1 + \frac{1}{2^n} + \frac{1}{3^n} + \frac{1}{4^n} + \cdots$$

which has meaning whenever $n$ is such that the series on the right converges. We know, for example, that if $n = 1$, the series

$$1 + \frac{1}{2} + \frac{1}{3} + \frac{1}{4} + \cdots$$

diverges, which means that no matter how large a number you specify, I can exceed it by taking a sufficiently great number of terms of the series.

There are important unsolved problems connected with the Zeta function and its complex extension, including the famous Riemann Hypothesis, a bit beyond our reach at this stage. One interesting problem, however, is readily stated. It turns out, strangely enough, that $\zeta(2), \zeta(4), \cdots \zeta(2n), \cdots$ are all rational multiples of even powers of $\pi$. We have

$$\zeta(2) = \frac{\pi^2}{6}$$

$$\zeta(4) = \frac{\pi^4}{90}$$

and so on. The general formula is

$$\zeta(2n) = \frac{2^{2n-1} |B_{2n}|}{(2n)!} \pi^{2n}$$

where the $B_{2n}$ are the Bernoulli Numbers, well known and possible to calculate in each case. The problem is to find an analogous "closed form" for the *odd* integral zetas, $\zeta(2n + 1)$. The books customarily state that no such expression is known at present. Recently strong evidence has been developed supporting the belief that no such expression can exist, but a proof is still lacking.

# Notes

The number refers to the corresponding page of the text

1. A word of apology for the title is in order. Not by any stretch of the imagination could this book be considered a summary of those topics which will be the major concern of tomorrow's mathematicians. Because of the limitations imposed by our efforts to keep the language non-technical, we have been unable to mention many, perhaps most, of the best problems which crowd the working mathematician's docket. Furthermore, it is the rash soothsayer indeed who ventures to predict the next turn of events in this ever-changing and expanding science.

7. In the following discussion we describe, with the aid of an ingenious example due to Schwarz, one of the difficulties involved in the attempt to define surface area of a curved surface.

How could you measure the length of a curved piece of string? This is not so difficult as finding the area of a piece of orange peel. The string can be straightened out, and measured with a yardstick; the orange peel cannot be flattened out. However, if we talk about a mathematical curve instead of a piece of string, we are neither permitted nor able to pick it up and straighten it out. What we can do is to find out its length by a *limiting process*. Perhaps you recall from your plane geometry days that that was the way you found, or rather *defined*, the perimeter of a circle. The method is first to inscribe a regular hexagon in the circle, and show how its perimeter can be precisely calculated. Then one inscribes a regular twelve-sided polygon, and again calculates its perimeter. Polygons of 24, 48, 96, . . . sides are then considered, and a method is described to show how their perimeters can continue to be calculated if the number of sides is repeatedly doubled. The next stage is the observation that the perimeters of the polygons *approach* the perimeter of the

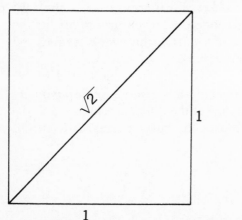

[36]

circle as the number of sides is increased. By this process one has not succeeded in writing down the exact length of the circumference; but two important things have been accomplished: (1) the length of the circumference has been *defined*, as a limit of known ascertainable lengths; and (2) the numerical value of the circumference's length can be found approximately, and that approximation can be made as close as we please by carrying the work to any specified number of decimal places.

In defining something in terms of a limit, one must be very careful. Suppose, for example, that we are interested in finding the length of the diagonal of a square one unit on a side (Figure 36). The Pythagorean theorem tells us that the square of the hypotenuse equals the sum of the squares of the other two sides, so that what we seek is of length $\sqrt{2}$. But $\sqrt{2}$, being irrational, is a somewhat elusive creature; and we might seek to evaluate it as follows. Draw the diagonal as if it were a staircase with a large number of very small equally spaced steps (Figure 37). Then

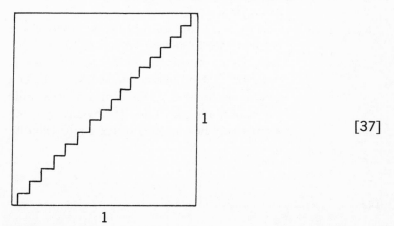

1

1

[37]

keep doubling and redoubling the number of steps. The step-diagonal may *look* as if it were approaching the actual diagonal as a limit. Indeed, we can bring any part of the stepped line to within as small a distance as we please of the original diagonal. But it is easy to see that it won't do as a measure of the *length* of the diagonal; for the length of the stepped line is always the total length of the horizontal elements (the treads) plus the total length of the vertical elements (the risers), or $1 + 1 = 2$, not $\sqrt{2}$.

"But that's a silly illustration," you say. "To guard against such an error we have only to specify that *both ends* of the broken lines that we use in the limit process lie on the original curve (or line). That was how we did the circle, and it worked: the vertices of the inscribed polygons were always points on the circle." And you are quite right. The length of a "smooth" curve can be defined as the limit of the sum of straight-line segments, each of whose lengths is made smaller in a definite specified way so that both ends of all of them always lie on the curve.

Why can't this concept be extended in the natural way to measuring surface areas? For many years mathematicians thought that it could be. Instead of straight-line segments one would use triangles, the simplest available pieces of plane area bounded by straight-line segments. The curved surface could then be triangulated, by laying out a set of points on the surface and joining them to neighboring points by straight lines. A spherical surface, for instance, could be approached by a sequence of inscribed polyhedra (not regular), such that all vertices of every polyhedron lay on the surface of the sphere. As the lengths of each individual side of each face of the polyhedron became smaller ("approached zero"), it was believed that the total area of the triangular faces would always have to approach the desired area of the curved surface (Figure 38). The necessary conditions were only that (1) the vertices of all triangles must always lie on the surface; (2) the number of triangles shall increase indefinitely; (3) the lengths of all sides of all triangles shall decrease indefinitely. But a definition, to have any value, must work *all* of the time, not only some of the time. H. A. Schwarz (1843–1921) produced a disconcerting example in which the triangles behaved in accordance with all of the three restrictions, and yet the surface

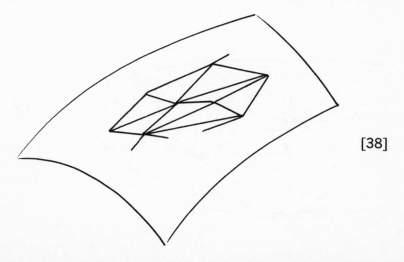

[38]

area of the inscribed polyhedron spectacularly failed to converge to the curved surface area. What is particularly impressive about Schwarz's example is that the curved surface is nothing fancy or crinkly, but one of the simplest and most innocent of surfaces, the lateral part of a right-circular cylinder. In fact this surface is developable from a plane, so that its area is known in advance.

We describe Schwarz's polyhedron. On the surface of a right-circular cylinder of height $h$ and radius $r$, select $2n$ vertical lines, equally spaced, and $2n^3$ horizontal equally spaced circles. Join alternate intersection points with straight-line segments as indicated in Figure 39. There are $4n^4$ triangles forming an "accordion-like" polyhedron inscribed in the cylinder. Now let $n$ become indefinitely large. All sides of all triangles tend toward zero, and certainly the vertices remain on the surface. But the planes of the triangles, like a closing accordion,

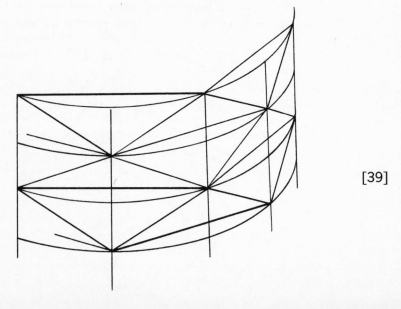

[39]

turn edgewise to the surface instead of approaching it tangentially; and the total surface area of the triangle-faced inscribed polyhedron becomes as large as you please, and tends to infinity instead of to $2\pi rh$. For a clear exposition of the mathematics involved, see p. 350, *Calculus,* John F. Randolph, Macmillan, 1955. (In all references, we shall systematically list the initial page number only.)

7. The Banach-Tarski theorem was published in *Fundamenta Mathematicae,* Vol. 6 (1924), p. 244.

7. Raphael Robinson, *Fundamenta Mathematicae,* Vol. 34 (1947), p. 246. See also *Amer. Math. Monthly,* Vol. 55 (1948), p. 459.

12. The proof that the general angle cannot be trisected with ruler and compass is completely developed in many places. See for instance *Ruler and Compasses,* by Hilda P. Hudson, p. 21. This is a Chelsea reprint (1953), bound together with *Squaring the Circle.* Also Felix Klein's *Famous Problems of Elementary Geometry,* Chelsea (1955), p. 5. Courant and Robbins, in *What is Mathematics?* (Oxford, 1941), give a somewhat more sophisticated treatment starting on p. 120.

14. The rectangle problem was suggested by H. D. and S. K. Stein, "On dividing an object efficiently," *Amer. Math. Monthly,* Vol. 63 (1956), p. 111. Another example, now classic, is the search for the solution to the problem of least area in which to reverse a line

segment in the plane. It is described in the author's *Through the Mathescope*, Oxford (1956), p. 79.

15. Gödel's theorem: "Uber formal unentscheidbare Sätze der Principia Mathematica und verwandter Systeme," *Monatshefte für Mathematik und Physik*, Vol. 38 (1931), p. 173.

15. Alonzo Church and A. M. Turing (separately) took the next logical step by showing that it is impossible to prescribe any systematic procedure for ascertaining whether a given proposition is Gödel-undecidable or not. Church, "An unsolvable problem of elementary number theory," *Amer. Journal Math.*, Vol. 58 (1936), p. 345. Turing, "On computable numbers," *Proc. London Math. Soc.*, (2) Vol. 42 (1937), p. 230.

18. The dispersal problem for $n = 5$ was solved for the plane circular disk by Eric. H. Neville, *Proc. London Math Soc.* (1914), p. 308; but he says nothing about $n > 5$. Inasmuch as the solution for $n = 5$ is not a regular pentagonal arrangement, each value of $n$ probably has to be investigated separately.

18. The value of $k$ in the dispersal problem on the disk does not change with every change in $n$. We encounter a surprise at the very first stage: $k = r$, the radius of the disk, whether $n = 1$ or $n = 2$. In other words, if we are trying to minimize the greatest distance from any point to the nearest defense unit in a circular country, one unit can do the job precisely as well as two.

# Notes

19. On p. 610 of *Amer. Math. Monthly,* Vol. 59 (1952), L. L. Whyte gives a list of unsolved problems associated with the dispersal and scattering problems. See also the footnote on p. 276 of H. S. M. Coxeter's new *Introduction to Geometry,* John Wiley & Sons, 1961.

20. Hugo Steinhaus, *Mathematical Snapshots,* new edition, Oxford, 1960, p. 322.

21. G. K. Wenceslas, *Amer. Math. Monthly,* Vol. 65 (1958), p. 775.

22. C. S. Ogilvy, "An interception problem," *Journal of the Institute of Navigation,* Vol. 5 (1956), p. 89.

23. The problems of the boats and swimmers were given to me by Stefan Burr, a graduate student at Princeton University. He believes them to be unsolved; if solved, the solutions have not been made known.

24. The quoted passage is from *Frontiers of Numerical Analysis,* edited by R. E. Langer, University of Wisconsin Press, 1960, p. 71.

26. The problem is closely allied with certain voting matrices. See Manfred Kochen, "A mathematical formulation of influence distributions in decision-making groups," *Journal Soc. Industrial and Applied Math.,* Vol. 6 (1958), p. 199.

28. Freund, "Round robin mathematics," *Amer. Math. Monthly,* Vol. 63 (1956), p. 112. The bridge problem is older: R. E. Moritz, *Amer. Math. Monthly,* Vol. 38 (1931), p. 340.

28. Another unsolved tournament problem is stated at the end of a paper by Francis

Scheid, *Amer. Math. Monthly,* Vol. 67 (1960), p. 39.

29. The quotation on the Traveling Salesman problem is from the discussion in *The New World of Math,* George A. W. Boehm, Dial Press, 1959. A solution for the U.S. problem (slightly modified) appears on p. 116.

29. Franz Hohn, "The mathematical aspects of switching," *Amer. Math. Monthly,* Vol. 62 (1955), p. 75.

31. C. E. Shannon, *Bell System Technical Journal,* Vol. 27 (1948), p. 379. The problem of implementing Shannon's Theorem is stated by H. H. Goldstine in a paper "Information theory," *Science,* Vol. 133 (1961), p. 1395.

32. *Frontiers of Numerical Analysis* (see note to p. 24), Zdenek Kopal, paper No. 3, "Numerical problems of contemporary celestial mechanics."

33. The postal savings problem was formulated by V. L. Klee, *Amer. Math. Monthly,* Vol. 56 (1949), p. 413.

36. "College admissions and the stability of marriage," D. Gale and L. S. Shapley, *Amer. Math. Monthly,* Vol. 69 (1962), p. 9.

37. Stanislav M. Ulam, at the Los Alamos Scientific Laboratories in New Mexico, has written No. 8 of the Interscience Tracts in Pure and Applied Mathematics, called *A Collection of Mathematical Problems,* Interscience, 1960. Several of our problems come from this book, which we shall hereafter refer to as "Ulam." The bridge problem is No. 9 on p. 36.

# Notes

38. Martin Gardner, whose column of mathematical games appears monthly in *Scientific American,* gave generous assistance in the compilation of this chapter.

38. In connection with the paradox, see G. C. Nerlich's paper, "Unexpected examinations and unprovable statements," *Mind,* Vol. 70 (1961), p. 503.

41. Leonard Euler, 1707–83, said to be the most prolific mathematician in history.

41. E. T. Parker, R. C. Bose, and S. S. Shrikhande solved the tenth-order problem, thus disproving Euler's conjecture. Their discovery made the front page of the *New York Times* (April 26, 1959), a most unusual occurrence for any topic in mathematics. Gardner's column in the November 1959 *Scientific American* gave the full story, and the front cover of the magazine carried a color picture of the $10 \times 10$ Graeco-Latin square of our Figure 9.

42. Note in connection with the subsquare of order 3: Interchanging the order (position) of any two rows or of any two columns of a Graeco-Latin square results in another Graeco-Latin square. But the people who work with these things consider that this is such a trivial change that they call two such squares the same square. This means that one cannot simply shift a column out of the subsquare to break it up: that doesn't count!

43. The polyomino problems are from an article by S. W. Golomb on "The general theory of polyominoes," in the August 1961

issue of a little magazine called *Recreational Mathematics* published in Idaho Falls, Idaho.

Very recently R. C. Read has determined the numbers of polyominoes of orders 8, 9, and 10; "Contributions to the cell growth problem," *Canadian Jour. Math.*, Vol. 14 (1962), p. 1. Read's hammer-and-tongs methods seem not to lead in the direction of a general formula for order *n*. See also F. Harary, "Unsolved problems in the enumeration of graphs," *Publ. Math. Inst. Hungarian Acad. Sci.*, Vol. 5 (1960), p. 63.

44. The theoretical machine used in Rado's problem of the three cards is a so-called *Turing machine,* after its inventor, A. M. Turing.

47. The problem of the balls is equivalent to a ranking problem discussed by Ford and Johnson, *Amer. Math. Monthly,* Vol. 66 (1959), p. 387.

47. The definition of the theory of games is quoted directly from *The Compleat Strategyst,* by J. D. Williams, McGraw-Hill, 1954, p. 215. The book is written entirely without mathematics, and is a noble effort to present a technical subject non-technically. There are times when it seems that the price is rather high: some passages suffer from a thirst which a short draught of mathematics could quickly quench. But on the whole, the book succeeds in its aim. At the opposite extreme, *The Theory of Games and Economic Behavior,* by John von Neumann and Oscar Morgenstern, Princeton, 1944, is rough going.

I cannot resist the temptation to tell a famous anecdote about von Neumann, who was one of the great intellects at the Institute for Advanced Study until his untimely death in 1957. A friend of his, out strolling with him one day, gave him the problem of the Industrious Bee (see the author's *Mathescope,* p. 39), which has a very simple solution if you happen to attack it from the proper angle. After walking on for a few steps, von Neumann turned to his companion and gave him the correct answer. His friend smiled and remarked, "You saw the trick because you are a mathematician. Most people try to solve it by summing convergent infinite series, which is quite a project." "I know," replied von Neumann, dryly, "that's what I just now did."

51. The tetrahedron problem: No. 4516, Victor Thebault, *Amer. Math. Monthly,* Vol. 59 (1952), p. 702.

52. The parabola problem: No. 4241, R. Goormaghtigh, *Amer. Math. Monthly,* Vol. 54 (1947), p. 168.

53. The Lebesgue covering problem, with no hint as to its possible solution, is mentioned, along with several others of this type, on p. 18 of *Convex Figures,* I. M. Yaglom and V. G. Boltyanskii, Holt, Rinehart and Winston, 1961. See also Ch. 6, *ibid.,* for further unsolved problems.

55. Figure of minimum area with given circumference and diameter: M. Scholander, "On certain minimum problems in the theory

of convex curves," *Trans. Amer. Math. Soc.*, Vol. 73 (1952), p. 139.

56. The two questions about the perpendicular chords are posed by Nicholas D. Kazarinoff in a book called *Analytic Inequalities,* Holt, Rinehart & Winston, 1961, p. 85. The first conjecture is due to Peter Ungar, of New York University.

56. Equichordal curves: G. Dirac, *Journal London Math. Soc.,* Vol. 27 (1952), p. 429. This paper indicates that there are probably no curves with two equichordal points.

57. Second convex surface swept out by point $P$: the problem is listed by Ulam, p. 38, where it is credited to Mazur.

57. H. Auerbach, *Studia Mathematica,* Vol. 7 (1938), p. 121. The Steinhaus comment is on p. 162 of the new edition of *Mathematical Snapshots.*

57. Ulam mentions the equilibrium problem (p. 38) and offers an allied problem: If a body rests in equilibrium in every position (orientation) on a flat horizontal surface, is it necessarily a sphere?

58. $n > 4$: Yaglom & Boltyanskii, p. 93.

59. Goldberg on rotors: *Amer. Math. Monthly,* Vol. 64 (1957), p. 76. Also *Mathematics of Computation,* Vol. 14 (1960), p. 235, where a list of thirty-six pertinent references is given.

59. Three concurrent chords at 60°. Steinhaus, *Polish Academy of Sciences,* Class 3, 1957, p. 595. Also *Mathematical Snapshots,* p. 162 of the new edition.

59. Non-bendability of a convex surface: Hilbert and Cohn-Vossen, *Geometry and the Imagination,* Chelsea, 1952, p. 230. Re-entrant polyhedra, *ibid.,* p. 290.

60. Moser's problem and the hexagonal diagram are from *Recreational Mathematics Magazine,* June 1961, p. 51. The equilateral triangle version is credited to Raphael Robinson. For recent results on map coloring problems, see W. T. Tutte in *Scripta Mathematica,* Vol. 25 (1961), p. 305.

61. The question on skew lines in 3-space was suggested by Littlewood. See also *Mathematical Puzzles and Diversions,* by Martin Gardner, Crowell 1961, p. 105.

61. Erdos's conjecture: see Moser, *Amer. Math. Monthly,* Vol. 59 (1952), p. 85.

62. The triangle question is asked by Kazarinoff, who conjectures that the answer is in the negative. *Analytic Inequalities,* p. 84.

63. The question about the maximum section of the tetrahedron has recently reappeared as Advanced Problem No. 5006, *Amer. Math. Monthly,* Vol. 69 (1962), p. 63.

64. A. R. Hyde, *Amer. Math. Monthly,* Vol. 63 (1956), p. 578.

64. Maximum section of a right-circular cylinder, *Amer. Math. Monthly,* Vol. 60 (1953), p. 715.

65. The dissection of the square into acute triangles is discussed by Gardner, *Scientific American,* March 1960, p. 178.

65. "Acute isosceles dissection of the obtuse

triangle," V. E. Hoggatt, Jr., and Russ Denman, *Amer. Math. Monthly,* Vol. 68 (1961), p. 912.

66. The dissection into twenty-four different squares, with a fascinating account of its discovery, is described in November 1958 *Scientific American,* p. 142. The problem has a direct connection with the flow of current in electrical networks, consideration of which led to its ultimate solution.

67. The table of Figure 22 is from p. 162 of November 1961 *Scientific American.*

67. The packing problem: C. A. Rogers, "The packing of equal spheres," *Proc. London Math. Soc.* (3) Vol. 8 (1958), p. 609. Also Coxeter, *Introduction to Geometry,* Wiley, 1961, p. 457

68. Four points on a surface: Orrin Frink, No. 4369, *Amer. Math. Monthly,* Vol. 56 (1949), p. 637.

68. Greenspan's problem: No. 4774, *Amer. Math. Monthly,* Vol. 65 (1958), p. 125.

69. Equilateral triangles: J. Gallego-Diaz, *Amer. Math. Monthly,* Vol. 60 (1953), p. 336.

69. Quadrilaterals: Josef Langr, *ibid.,* p. 551.

71. The quotations are from "Thebault—the number theoretist," by E. P. Starke, part of a tribute published in the October 1947 *Amer. Math. Monthly,* Vol. 54, p. 443. The quoted problem is No. 3886, p. 482 of Vol. 45.

74. Pierre de Fermat, 1601–65.

74. The formulas for all primitive Pythago-

# Notes

rean triples are given in Courant and Robbins, *What is Mathematics?*, p. 41.

76. Very recently an amateur mathematician named von Ammon has developed a new kind of sieve which he calls a *scanner,* to test very large numbers for primality without lengthy computations and without resort to a computer. A complete description of the device was still in course of preparation in 1962; but its success, at least for some purposes, has already been assured. For instance, von Ammon was able to list eighty-five "new" primes of the form $n^2 - 2$ between 100,000,000 and 121,000,000. The list was checked by the data-processing division of the IBM Corporation with the use of a computer, and found to be 100% correct. (Frederic von Ammon, 5404 N.E. 22 Ave., Fort Lauderdale, Florida.)

78. G. A. Paxson. The quotation is from a letter from Raphael Robinson to the author, dated February 11, 1961.

78. See "A report on primes of the form $k \cdot 2^n + 1$ and on factors of Fermat numbers," R. M. Robinson, *Proc. Amer. Math. Soc.,* Vol. 9 (1958), p. 473.

78. The "new conjecture" about Mersenne primes was suggested, probably by Emory P. Starke, on p. 278 of Vol. 64 (1957), *Amer. Math. Monthly.*

79. The Lucas and Ball quotations are found in the 1955 Chelsea reprint of Klein's *Famous Problems of Elementary Geometry,* p. 81

*et seq.* The references found therein are not up to date.

81. $F_7$ and $F_8$ were tested for factors up to the limit of a program which Robinson happened to have running on the SWAC, with the results stated.

81. Factors of the numbers consisting of $n$ 1's are discussed in *Recreational Mathematics,* October 1961, p. 57. Lines 10–11 of that page should read: "However, for the following 13 cases of composites, the factors of the resulting number are unknown: 37, 43, . . . ."

84. The proof of the prime number property of Pascal's Triangle is given in the author's *Through the Mathescope,* p. 137.

84. The problem stated at the end of this section is equivalent to E 1145, *Amer. Math. Monthly,* Vol. 61 (1954), p. 712.

85. "Some conjectures associated with the Goldbach conjecture." Under this title, I. A. Barnett and Ted Cook of the University of Cincinnati, wrote:

"The first conjecture, a stronger form of the Goldbach conjecture for odd numbers, says that every odd number $2k - 1 = x + 2y$, where $x$ and $y$ are primes, $k \geqslant 4$. The second conjecture is that it is possible to find a representation of every odd number of the form $6k + 1$ or $6k + 5$ as $2x' + 3y'$ ($x', y'$ prime) $k \geqslant 3$, for which either the $x'$ or the $y'$ appears as one of the primes in *some* representation of $2k - 1$ as the sum of a prime plus the double of a prime. Both conjectures have been verified to about 15000." *Amer. Math. Monthly,* Vol. 68 (1961), p. 711.

86. The quotations are from Ulam, p. 120.

87. The second Ulam sequence was communicated to the author by letter, March 22, 1961.

88. The problem of the pairs of prime reversals was suggested by I. A. Barnett.

89. For further discussion of the decimalization of $1/7$, see Ch. 2 of *Through the Mathescope.*

89. Other interesting questions involve the study of the repeating decimals of the reciprocals of primes which are not maximal. J. C. Severn, of Toledo, Ohio, has devised methods of pinpointing periods of certain lengths. He has supplied (in a letter to the author, 1960) the following list of all primes $p$ for which the decimal expansion of $1/p$ has the indicated period length. According to Severn, no further primes with these periods can exist. The work is of course based on numerical analysis, not mere trial, using nothing more elaborate than a desk calculator.

For those interested in pursuing the problem of the numbers consisting only of consecutive 1's. Severn points out the following helpful fact. Let $q$ be a period length. Then if $q$ is itself a prime greater than 3, we find that in each case the product of all the primes $p$ whose period length is $q$ is the number consisting of exactly $q$ 1's. Thus the two problems are really two aspects of one problem.

An (incomplete) table extending Severn's

| List of all primes with reciprocals of period length less than 17 | |
|---|---|
| Period | Prime |
| 1 | 3 |
| 2 | 11 |
| 3 | 37 |
| 4 | 101 |
| 5 | 41, 271 |
| 6 | 7, 13 |
| 7 | 239, 4649 |
| 8 | 73, 137 |
| 9 | 333667 |
| 10 | 9091 |
| 11 | 21649, 513239 |
| 12 | 9901 |
| 13 | 53, 79, 265371653 |
| 14 | 909091 |
| 15 | 31, 2906161 |
| 16 | 17, 5882353 |

up to period length 100 was published in 1874 by the same William Shanks who calculated, by hand, the value of pi to 707 decimals. *Proceedings of the Royal Society,* Vol. 22, p. 382.

Gauss's *Werke,* Band 2, p. 412, lists all of the decimal expansions of reciprocals of primes less than 1000, and of the powers of primes.

A baseball enthusiast once told me that he had discovered empirically in his calculations of batting averages that the length of the period of a non-maximal prime $p$ is always a factor of $p - 1$.

If $p$ is a maximal prime, then the length of the period for $p^m$ is $p^m - p$.

90. $n! + 1$: *Amer. Math. Monthly,* Vol. 58 (1951), p. 193.

91. There is an excellent treatment of Waring's problem in Rademacher and Toeplitz, *The Enjoyment of Mathematics,* Princeton University Press, 1957, Ch. 9. See also the notes to Ch. 9, p. 198, *ibid.,* for further information and references.

91. L. J. Mordell, *Reflections of a Mathematician,* Canadian Math. Congress, 1959, p. 19. The conjecture is discussed further on p. 97 of the present book.

92. Perfect numbers: see Rademacher and Toeplitz, Ch. 19.

93. Abundant numbers: *Amer. Math. Monthly,* Vol. 57 (1950), p. 561.

94. The Dickson remark is from the *History,* Vol. 2, p. 647.

95. The first problem on consecutive powers is from *Amer. Math. Monthly,* Vol. 39 (1932), p. 175. See also Dickson, Vol. 2, p. 585. The extended problem is from *Amer. Math. Monthly,* Vol. 45 (1938), p. 253. The third problem is from Vol. 47 (1940), *ibid.,* p. 182.

96. The set of fourteen Diophantine problems came from the following sources:

1, 2, 3, 4, 5, 8, and 9 are from a paper by W. Sierpinski "On some unsolved problems of arithmetics," *Scripta Mathematica*, Vol. 25 (1960), p. 125, except for the questions on asymptotic density which I threw in at no extra charge. Sierpinski lists many more in addition to these.

6, 7, and 10 are posed by Mordell, *Journal London Math. Soc.*, Vol. 28 (1953), p. 500.

11, 12, and 13 were given to me by I. A. Barnett of the University of Cincinnati, in 1961.

14 is Mordell's. *Journal London Math. Soc.*, Vol. 36 (1961), p. 355.

99. The general cubic problem is from Mordell, *Reflections of a Mathematician*, p. 32.

99. Davenport: *Journal London Math. Soc.*, Vol. 35 (1960), p. 141.

99. The rectangular parallelepiped question was raised in 1955 (*Amer. Math. Monthly*, Vol. 62, p. 494); but it had been kicking around for a long time before that.

100. Walker's problem: Nos. 4326 and 4327, *Amer. Math. Monthly*, Vol. 56 (1949), p. 39.

100. Stefan Burr of Princeton says he has the conjecture about 144 "almost" proved. For further properties of the Fibonacci numbers presented on an elementary level, see *Fibonacci Numbers,* by N. N. Vorobev, Random House, 1961.

102. "Is such a grid possible?" No.

104. That four colors are sufficient to color a map of thirty-four or fewer countries was proved by Philip Franklin of M.I.T., *Journal of Mathematics and Physics,* Vol. 16 (1937), p. 172.

105. Steinhaus, *Mathematical Snapshots,* has a clearly drawn diagram of a torus map requiring seven colors on p. 296.

107. Ulam, p. 50.

108. The problem of the fixed point property is outlined by R. H. Bing, on p. 41 of *Elementary Point Set Topology,* No. 8 of the Slaught Memorial Papers, published by the Mathematical Association of America, 1960. The next problem is on p. 28, *ibid.* The 1948 reference is to E. E. Moise, "An indecomposable plane continuum which is homeomorphic to each of its non-degenerate sub-continua," *Trans. Amer. Math. Soc.,* Vol. 63 (1948), p. 581.

109. Enlacement: Ulam, p. 46.

109. Lines of force: Ulam, p. 108.

114. Hawthorne's problem: *Amer. Math. Monthly,* Vol. 62 (1955), p. 40.

114. The coins: *Ibid.,* Vol. 48 (1941), p. 483.

115. The stamp- and map-folding prob-

lems are from *The New World of Math,* pp. 114 and 75, respectively.

115. Abstract combinatorial problem: *Amer. Math. Monthly,* Vol. 51 (1944), p. 534.

116. *The Caliban problem.* The probability of drawing $k$ red balls from a bag containing $n$ balls of which $r$ are red is $p = {}_rC_k/{}_nC_k$. One sees at once by expanding the $C$'s that $p = \frac{1}{2}$ whenever $n = 2k$ and $r = 2k - 1$:

$$p = \frac{(2k - 1)(2k - 2)\cdots(2k - k + 1)(2k - k)}{2k(2k - 1)(2k - 2)\cdots(2k - k + 1)}$$

$$= \frac{1}{2}$$

For $k = 5$ we have the Caliban answer. The question remains whether it is possible to obtain $\frac{1}{2}$ with less cancellation of the factors. One finds by trial that there are always too many prime factors. We display the information for $p$ near $\frac{1}{2}$ in a table. The number in the left-hand column of each row is the number of factors in the numerator of $p$ which are to cancel completely by occurring also in the denominator.

| | $k = 5$ | $k = 6$ |
|---|---|---|
| 0 | This requires a sequence of $2k$ composite integers in the vicinity of 50. No such sequence exists. | |
| 1 | $\dfrac{_{28}C_5}{_{32}C_5} < \dfrac{1}{2} < \dfrac{_{29}C_5}{_{33}C_5}$ | $\dfrac{_{43}C_6}{_{48}C_6} < \dfrac{1}{2} < \dfrac{_{44}C_6}{_{49}C_6}$ |
| 2 | $\dfrac{_{22}C_5}{_{25}C_5} < \dfrac{1}{2} < \dfrac{_{23}C_5}{_{26}C_5}$ | $\dfrac{_{35}C_6}{_{39}C_6} < \dfrac{1}{2} < \dfrac{_{36}C_6}{_{40}C_6}$ |
| 3 | * | $\dfrac{_{27}C_6}{_{30}C_6} < \dfrac{1}{2} < \dfrac{_{28}C_6}{_{31}C_6}$ |
| 4 | The Caliban case: $\dfrac{_9C_5}{_{10}C_5} = \dfrac{1}{2}$ | * |
| 5 | | The Caliban case: $\dfrac{_{11}C_5}{_{12}C_5} = \dfrac{1}{2}$ |

For the cases marked * we consider general $k$ and ask that all but 2 factors cancel in their entirety, leaving

$$\frac{(n-k)(n-k-1)}{n(n-1)} = \frac{1}{2}$$

solving this quadratic for $k$ yields:

$$k = \frac{2n - 1 \pm \sqrt{2n^2 - 2n + 1}}{2}$$

The discriminant must equal a perfect square, say $m^2$. Solving that now for $n$ in terms of $m$, we find

$$n = \tfrac{1}{2}(1 \pm \sqrt{2m^2 - 1})$$

The various $m$ which make $2m^2 - 1$ a perfect square are well known to be the denominators of every second convergent of the continued fraction development of $\sqrt{2}$.

The first (usable) $m$ is 5, which says that $n = 4$, $k = 1$, $r = 2$ constitute a solution. It is the rather trivial one of drawing one ball from a bag containing two reds and two others. Clearly $p = \frac{1}{2}$.

The next (usable) $m$ is 29; $n = 21$, $k = 6$, $r = 19$. Thus the probability of drawing six red balls from a bag containing nineteen reds and two others is $\frac{1}{2}$. We note that this is *in addition* to the Caliban case, one of which occurs for every $k$. Thus the solution of (2) is not unique; but we have also proven that 5 is not a suitable $k$, allowing the conclusion that the solution of (1) is unique.

We have also located some other $k$ for which the solution is surely not unique, the next one being $k = 35$, for which the pair $n = 120$, $r = 118$ is a solution.

There remains unanswered the question:

# Notes

For what additional $k$ is the solution non-unique because all but 3, or all but 4, or all but ... $k$ factors cancel completely? The general Diophantine equations for these cases are of degree 3, 4, ... $k$ respectively, and are consequently untidy.

117. The problem of the fewest intersections is discussed by Richard K. Guy in *NABLA*, the journal of the Malayan Mathematical Society, Singapore, June, 1960, p. 68. Compare also the problem of the Three Eccentric Professors, *Through the Mathescope*, p. 126.

121. Ulam, No. 5, p. 40.

123. "The number of terms in the expansion of an infinite determinant," A. W. Goodman, *Amer. Math. Monthly*, Vol. 55 (1948), p. 419.

123. Kurt Gödel, "What is Cantor's continuum problem?", *Amer. Math. Monthly*, Vol. 54 (1947), p. 515.

124. New hypotheses which imply the continuum hypothesis: *Notices of the Amer. Math. Soc.*, Vol. 8 No. 1, (1961), p. 55, 61-T-9.

125. Tibor Rado, "The problem of least area," *Mathematische Zeitschrift*, Vol. 32 (1930), p. 763.

125. Jesse Douglas, "Solution of the problem of Plateau," *Trans. Amer. Math. Soc.*, Vol. 33 (1931), p. 263.

126. H. D. and S. K. Stein, "On dividing an object efficiently," *Amer. Math. Monthly*, Vol. 63 (1956), p. 111.

126. Lines cutting off ⅓ of the area of a tri-

angle. The problem is no longer unsolved. After the book had gone to the printer, a complete solution by V. E. Hoggatt, Jr., was published in *Amer. Math. Monthly,* Vol. 69 (1962), p. 98.

127. Minimal surfaces in a wire cube. Courant and Robbins, *What is Mathematics?,* pp. 387, 397, 502. Also see Fig. 212, p. 549 of D'Arcy Thompson, *On Growth and Form,* Cambridge, 1952.

128. The minimal motion problems are quoted in their entirety from Ulam, p. 79, No. 9.

129. The hanging chain: John Disch in *Amer. Math. Monthly,* Vol. 59 (1952), p. 329.

132. The three problems of Erdos. (1) *Amer. Math. Monthly,* Vol. 56 (1949), p. 343. (2) No. 3835 in the *Dunkel Memorial Problem Book* published by the Mathematical Association of America in 1957. (3) Ulam, p. 27, No. 9.

133. Smallest coefficients: *Amer. Math. Monthly,* Vol. 57 (1950), p. 264.

134. This definition of a function is neither complete nor rigorous, but it will suffice for the moment.

136. The quoted line is from Konrad Knopp, *Infinite Sequences and Series,* Dover, 1956, p. 122.

136. The zeta function can be extended to the complex domain. The Riemann hypothesis, as yet unproven, states that all the zeros of this function have real part $= \frac{1}{2}$.

137. For material on $\zeta(2n)$ see for instance Knopp, p. 173.

137. The "strong evidence" on $\zeta(2n + 1)$ is the work of Rolfe P. Ferguson, an undergraduate at Hamilton College, who has conducted a remarkably thorough independent investigation of the problem. The situation seems (very roughly) analogous to trying to find a Fourier series expansion for an odd function in terms of cosines only.

# Index

# Index

## B

balls
    of different weights, 47, 150
    five red, 116
Ball, W. W. Rouse, 79, 155
Banach and Tarski, 7, 124, 145
Barnett, I. A., 156, 157, 160
bee problem, 151
*Bell System Technical Journal,* 148
bendability of surfaces, 59, 153
Bernoulli numbers, 137
billiards, 61
Bing, R. H., 161
binomial coefficients, 82
boat and swimmer problems, 23
boat racing problem, 25
Boehm, G. A. W., 148
Boltyanskii, V. G., 151, 152
Boolean algebra, 29
Bose, R. C., 149
bridge circuit, 30
bridge, game of, 28, 37, 147
Brouwer, L. E. J., 107
Burr, Stefan, 147, 161

## C

Caliban, 116, 162
*Canadian Journal of Mathematics,* 150
Cantor, Georg, 122, 165
cardinals, 122
cards, problem of three, 111
catenary, 128
centroids, locus of, 69
chain, hanging, 128, 166

# Index

# Index

# Index

## G

Gale, D., 148

Gallego-Diaz, J., 154

game theory, 37, 47, 150

games, mathematical, Ch. 3

Gardner, Martin, 38, 104, 149, 153

Gaskell, Robert E., 33

Gaussian integers, 95

Gauss, Karl Friedrich, 158

geometric progression, 11

geometric systems, 9

geometry, Ch. 4

*Geometry and the Imagination*, 153

glove, 101

Gödel, Kurt, 15, 123, 146, 165

Goldbach's conjecture, 85, 98, 156

Goldberg, Michael, 59, 152

Goldstine, H. H., 148

Golomb, S. W., 149

Goodman, A. W., 165

Goormaghtigh, R., 151

Graeco-Latin squares, 40, 149

Greenspan, Donald, 68, 154

Guy, Richard K., 165

## H

Harary, F., 150

Hawthorne, Frank, 114, 161

headmaster's dilemma, 38

hexagon, regular, 60, 63

Hilbert and Cohn-Vossen, 59, 153

*History of the Theory of Numbers*, 94

Hoggatt, V. E. Jr., 154, 166

Hohn, Franz, 148

# Index

# Index

## L

Langer, R. E., 147
Langr, Josef, 154
latitude-longitude grid, 102
least covering area, 53
Lebesgue, 53, 151
Lemoine point, 51
limit, 140
Littlewood, J. E., 153
locus, 69
logarithm, 84
Lucas, Edouard, 79, 155
lucky numbers, 86

## M

machine, Turing, 45
Malayan Mathematical Society, 165
map coloring problems, 60, 103
map folding problem, 115
*Mathematical Puzzles and Diversions,* 153
*Mathematical Snapshots,* 147, 152
*Mathematics of Computation,* 152
*Mathematische Zeitschrift,* 165
maximum ride problem, 20
Mazur, 152
measure theory, 6
Mersenne numbers, 77, 93, 155
*Mind,* 149
minimal
    curves, 13, 14
    motion, 127
    surfaces, 127
mixed strategy, 48
Möbius band, 5

# Index

# Index

# Index

# Index

# Index

Tutte, W. T., 153
twin primes, 85
two-person games, 48

## U

Ulam, Stanislav M., 37, 85, 107, 121, 148, 152, 157, 161, 165, 166
undecidable problems, 15, 146
Ungar, Peter, 152

## V

variational problems, Ch. 9
volume, 7
von Ammon, Frederic, 155
von Neumann, John, 48, 150
Vorobev, N. N., 161

## W

Walker, R. J., 100, 160
Waring's problem, 91, 159
weighing problem, 47
Wenceslas, G. K., 147
*What is Mathematics?*, 127, 145, 155, 166
Whyte, L. L., 147
Williams, J. D., 150
*World Almanac,* 34

## Y

Yaglom, I. M., 151, 152

## Z

zeta function, 136, 166, 167